HOW
LIFE
BEGAN

creation *versus* evolution

ROY A. GALLANT

Four Winds Press

New York

1975

For
E. B., an enlightened editor,
and
E. J. K., an enlightened biologist

Title page illustration: Chap-Pek, the toad, the Aztec symbol for Earth. From an ancient Mexican funeral box for ashes.

LIBRARY OF CONGRESS CATALOGING IN PUBLICATION DATA

Gallant, Roy A.
How life began.

Bibliography: p.
SUMMARY: Surveys various myths and scientific hypotheses concerning the origin of the physical universe and of life on the planet Earth.
1. Life—Origin. 2. Evolution. 3. Creation.
[1. Life—Origin. 2. Evolution. 3. Creation]
I. Title.
QH325.G34 575.01′6 75–12996
ISBN 0–590–17363–4

575

PUBLISHED BY FOUR WINDS PRESS
A DIVISION OF SCHOLASTIC MAGAZINES, INC.,
NEW YORK, N.Y.
COPYRIGHT © 1975 BY ROY GALLANT
ALL RIGHTS RESERVED
PRINTED IN THE UNITED STATES OF AMERICA
LIBRARY OF CONGRESS CATALOG CARD NUMBER: 75–12996
1 2 3 4 5 79 78 77 76 75

CONTENTS

✺✺✺

Acknowledgments ✺ vi

1

ON THE FRINGE OF INTELLIGENCE ✺ 1
    The Primitive World of "Great Time" ✺ 2
    Man the Myth Maker ✺ 8
    Invention of the Gods ✺ 11
    How Myths Give Form to the World ✺ 13

2

IN THE BEGINNING . . . ✺ 17
    According to the Enuma Elish ✺ 17
    Creation of the World ✺ 18
    Creation of Life ✺ 24
    Classifying Creation Myths ✺ 29
    According to the
       Judeo-Christian Tradition ✺ 37
    Creation of the World and Life ✺ 38
    The Universal Flood ✺ 44
    Breaking with the Past ✺ 48

3

FROM MYTHS TO ATOMS ✺ 51
    Searching for the "World-Stuff" ✺ 52
    "On the Nature of Things" ✺ 57

4

A NEW BEGINNING: THE UNIVERSE ❈ 65

Enter Copernicus ❈ 66
Placing the Solar System in Time ❈ 71
Forming the Solar System in Space ❈ 76
Stars: The Element Factories ❈ 83
An Age for the Universe ❈ 88
A Steady-State Universe ❈ 89
A Big-Bang Universe ❈ 90

5

A NEW BEGINNING: LIFE ❈ 94

Spontaneous Generation ❈ 95
Fossils: Links with the Past ❈ 101
And Let There Be Life II ❈ 109

6

THE EVIDENCE FOR EVOLUTION ❈ 122

Enter Darwin ❈ 122
Earlier Evolutionists ❈ 126
Catastrophism and Special Creation ❈ 128
Voyage of H.M.S. Beagle ❈ 133
A Time for Decision ❈ 143

7

THE CREATIONISTS' STAND ❈ 152

Creation, Evolution, and Faith ❈ 154
Interpreting the Fossil Record ❈ 155
Catastrophism Revived ❈ 158
What Is a Species? ❈ 160
From Variation to Similarity ❈ 162
Battle of the Bones ❈ 163

8

THE EVOLUTIONISTS' STAND ❀ 171
  The Scientific Community Responds ❀ 171
  Design ❀ 173
  Catastrophism ❀ 175
  Ideal Type ❀ 180
  Can Creationism Undermine Biology? ❀ 182
  Accounting for Diversity ❀ 186

9

OF LIFE "OUT YONDER IN THE DARK" ❀ 189
  When Is a Thing a Living Thing? ❀ 190
  Life on Other Worlds ❀ 194

Books for Further Reading ❀ 201

Index ❀ 207
❀❀❀

ACKNOWLEDGMENTS

I wish to thank several individuals and publishers, in some instances for reading and commenting on various chapters, and in others for permission to use already published materials. In those instances where selected quotations were extremely brief and permission to use them, therefore, was not required, I acknowledge the source for those readers who may wish to refer to the original document in its entirety.

The quotations from Thorkild Jacobsen are from his account of the *Enuma Elish,* in *The Intellectual Adventure of Ancient Man,* by H. and H. A. Frankfort, John A. Wilson, Thorkild Jacobsen, and William A. Irwin, Copyright © The University of Chicago Press, 1946. Those passages from the *Enuma Elish* itself are from A. Heidel's translation of *The Babylonian Genesis,* The University of Chicago Press, 1951.

The account of the Pomo Indian creation myth on pages 30–32 is based on J. de Angulu's account in the *Journal of American Folklore,* vol. 48.

My thanks to Funk & Wagnalls Company for permisssion to reprint the Yuchi Indian creation myth appearing in Maria Leach's delightful book *The Beginning,* Copyright © by Funk & Wagnalls Company, 1956, retold by her from the W. O. Toggle Collection in the Bureau of American Ethnology in John R. Swanton's *Myths and Tales of the Southeastern Indians.*

My thanks also to Penguin Books, Ltd. for their permission to use selected passages from R. E. Latham's translation of Lucretius's *On The Nature of the Universe* (Penguin Classics,

1951) pp. 27–45, 55–59, 90–95, Copyright © R. E. Latham, 1951.

My thanks also to Doubleday & Company, Inc. for permission to use brief selections from my own books: *Charles Darwin, the Making of a Scientist,* Copyright © 1972, by Roy A. Gallant; *Man's Reach for the Stars,* Copyright © 1971, by Roy A. Gallant; *Exploring the Planets,* Copyright © 1958, 1967, by Doubleday & Company, Inc.; *Discovering Rocks and Minerals* (written in collaboration with Christopher J. Schuberth), Copyright © 1964, by Doubleday & Company, Inc.; also for permission to use a brief selection from *The Wonderful World of Prehistoric Animals,* by William Elgin Swinton, Copyright © 1961, by Rathbone Books, Ltd., and a new revised edition, Copyright © 1969, by Aldus Books, Ltd., London, and published in the United States by Doubleday & Company, Inc.

My special thanks to the National Association of Biology Teachers, Inc. for permission to use selections from the following articles appearing in their magazine, *The American Biology Teacher:* Garrett Hardin's paper, "Ambivalent Aspects of Evolution," 35(1): 15; Theodosius Dobzhansky's paper, "Nothing in Biology Makes Sense Except in the Light of Evolution," 35(3): 125; Richard P. Aulie's two-part article, "The Doctrine of Special Creation," 34(4): 194 and 34(5): 261; and Adrian M. Wenner's article, "Adam and Eve in Science," 35(5): 278.

My thanks also to The Institute for Creation Research Publishing Company for permission to use selected passages from Duane T. Gish's *Evolution, the Fossils Say No!* Copyright 1973, by ICR Publishing Company. Also to Zondervan Publishing House for permission to use brief passages from *Biology: A Search for Order in Complexity,* edited by John N. Moore and Harold Slusher, Copyright © 1970, 1974, by The Zondervan Corporation.

The two quotations from Loren Eiseley, on pages 199 and 200 are from his book, *The Immense Journey*, Copyright 1946, 1950, 1951, 1958, © 1956, 1957, by Loren Eiseley, and published by Random House.

The brief selection from Stephen Dole and Isaac Asimov on page 199 is from their book, *Planets for Man*, published by Random House and Copyright © 1964, by The Rand Corporation.

The Cyril Ponnamperuma quotation on page 189 is from *Exobiology*, edited by Cyril Ponnamperuma, Copyright © 1972, by North-Holland Publishing Company.

The Robert Jastrow quotation on page 67 is from his book, *Red Giants and White Dwarfs*, Copyright © 1967, by Robert Jastrow, and published by Harper & Row.

The A. I. Oparin quotations on pages *ix* and 51 are from his book, *The Origin of Life on the Earth*, published by Academic Press, Inc., 1957.

The H. S. Bellamy quotation on page 17 is from his book, *Moon, Myths, and Man*, Copyright 1938, by Harper and Brothers, Publishers.

The George Gaylord Simpson quotation on pages 123–124 is from his book (written with William S. Beck), *Life: An Introduction to Biology*, Copyright © 1965, by Harcourt Brace Jovanovich, Inc.

My particular thanks to biologist Dr. Edward J. Kormondy, Provost of The Evergreen State College, and to astronomer Dr. Mark R. Chartrand III, Director of The American Museum-Hayden Planetarium, for reading and offering valuable criticisms of various chapters.

ꙮ *Marduk, the Babylonian creation god, from a wall carving in Nineveh.*

"But who shall dwell in these worlds if they are inhabited? . . . Are we or they the Lords of the World?   —Kepler (1571–1630)

"*Every man, whatever his stage of development, has, consciously or unconsciously, put [the question of the origin on Earth of the first living things] to himself and found some sort of answer to it, for without some such answer one cannot form even the most primitive picture of the world.*"
—A. I. Oparin (1957)

1

ON THE FRINGE OF INTELLIGENCE

Out of the mists of time,
  To put his troubled mind at ease
Man has spun a thousand fantasies,
  And with them veiled his gaze
  Against Nature's cold, purposeless ways.

Who can conjure up two more haunting questions than "How did the world begin?" and "How did life arise?"

Is there a thinking person among us who has not, if only for a fleeting instant, felt the great weight of those ageless questions? Questions first framed countless sunrises ago by that inventor of language we call man.

How well I can remember, when, as a boy of fourteen, after turning out my reading lamp at bedtime, I gradually was consumed by the dark, that other world of haunted forests abounding with monstrous night creatures lingering from ages past in the dusty attics of our minds. But it was a monster of a different sort that tormented me—*time*, the mystery of eternity, time without a beginning or without end. The trap I had fallen into, of course, was trying to experience in my imagination something beyond human experience. I was trying to project myself out of measurable time and into the higher order of timelessness. But like all other modern men I am a prisoner locked into the framework of measurable time. The harder I tried to escape from it and into the higher order of timelessness, the more frustrated I became. It grew into a nightly ritual and, in effect, was an attempt to recapture the timelessness of primitive man. Then each morning after a troubled sleep I was rescued by that very time I was trying to escape from, but deep down I knew I would be drawn into the quicksands again in only a few hours.

Soon enough, however, the monster left me as suddenly as it had appeared. But over the years it has made other, although less frequent, visits. The most recent one took place several years ago when I had occasion to visit J. B. Priestley in his London home. Priestley said that he wanted to write a book about man and time, and as he spoke I felt my monster stir within. In Priestley had I found a soul mate? So it seemed, for he spoke of being a "time haunted man addressing himself chiefly to all those people [I know] from experience to be also Time-haunted."

❀❀❀

THE PRIMITIVE WORLD OF "GREAT TIME"

❀❀❀

But why begin this book about the origin of the Universe and the origin of life by talking about *time*? It is important, I think essential, to pry open a crack into the mind of primitive man to gain at least a glimpse of how he perceived the world with his mind's eye. The stage in man's development as a reasoning animal that we must return to occurred long before the birth of Jesus, long before the Golden Age of Greece

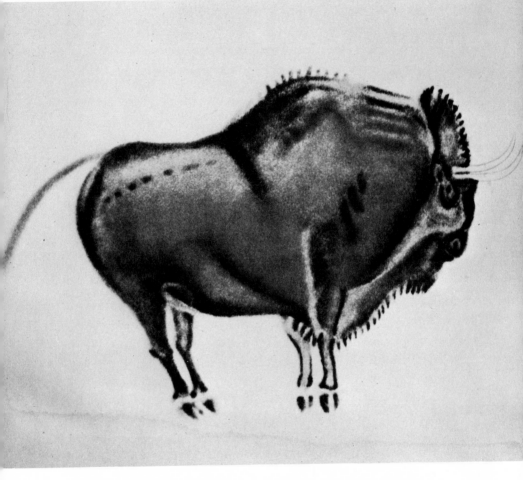

✻ *Cave paintings from prehistoric times, like this one from Altamira, Spain, some 20,000 years old, appear not to have been works of art for their own sake. Instead, they seem to have served the magical purpose of bringing luck to the hunters. Here were beings who had fashioned complex speech, which enabled them to discuss, plan, and reflect on their activities.*

some 300 years earlier, and long before those ancient peoples known as Sumerians left the first known writing on clay tablets more than 5,000 years ago. The men of timelessness who here concern us lived many thousands of years earlier still, before farming and the domestication of animals had come into practice some 10,000 to 15,000 years ago. It was a time when men lived in tribes and subsisted by food gathering and hunting. It was a time when men had mastered the art of using and making simple tools and had developed language far enough to plan and discuss the day's hunting activities.

According to some physical anthropologists, a brain size of about 700 to 800 cubic centimeters is needed for speech to be well enough developed to carry on the many activities required of people living in communities. Your brain size is roughly twice that. Java Man, Pekin Man, and Neanderthal Man all had brains large enough to qualify them as fluent users of language. Java Man and Pekin Man both lived from about 500,000 years ago to about 250,000 years ago but then mysteriously became extinct, as did a number of other ancestors of modern man. That places them near the middle of that geologic time period know as the Pleistocene, which began about 2 million years ago. Neanderthal Man is more recent, having lived in Europe and Asia between about 100,000 years ago and 45,000 years ago.

Although we can never know for certain how these people saw the world with their mind's eye, we can gain some clues by studying primitive peoples whose cultures today are little changed from what they were thousands of years ago. One such culture is that of the Australian aborigines, who recognize two kinds of time. One is *passing-time,* time that cannot be turned backward and that can be reckoned by the apparent motions of the Moon, Sun, and stars and by mechanically contrived

Reconstruction of heads of:
Java Man

Peking Man

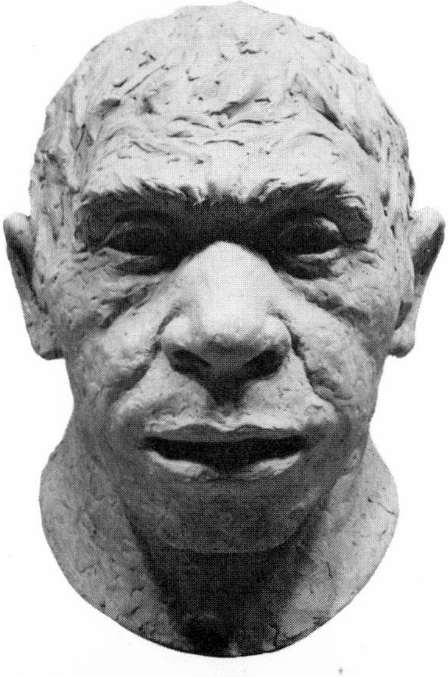

Neanderthal Man

COURTESY: THE AMERICAN MUSEUM OF NATURAL HISTORY, PHOTO BY THE AUTHOR

devices. The other, and to them the much more important kind of time, is called the *Great Time* in which past and future are magically blended with the present. When various primitive groups living today perform their ceremonial rites, often dressed in the costumes of the heroes of their myths, they work themselves into a frenzy through chants or through dancing or sometimes with the aid of drugs that induce hallucinations, and they enter that other world of Great Time and become one with their night creatures of eternity. The Zuni Indians of the American Southwest have their Masked God Society. When a Zuni puts on a mask, he believes that he enters Great Time and becomes a god. Carlos Castaneda, in his three books about how he, as a young student, subjected himself for several years to the teachings of a sorcerer, was writing about Great Time, about those other-worldly events perceived with the mind's eye when we throw off the confining cloak of passing-time. He called that world of the imagination a "separate reality." It is that dark corner of the mind where man invents the gods and demons that inhabit his myths.

The French psychologist Jean Piaget tells us that the ability of young children to invent fanciful stories undoubtedly has its roots in the mind of early man. Only later in life do we enter the world of rational thought. But even then that dark region of the mind echoing the past comes to our rescue every now and then by putting the world right again when it has somehow gone wrong. For instance, the cool night air flowing in through my bedroom window when I'm sleeping chills me, but not quite enough to awaken me. The world has gone wrong because I sense that I am cold but am helpless to correct the situation because I am still asleep. However, things are quickly put right when my myth-making faculty comes to the rescue

A ceremonial mask from New Guinea (the island of New Ireland).

and makes me dream. I dream that it is snowing and that I'm outside without my jacket. "Naturally you're cold!" my sleeping self says, and so the problem is dismissed. Although the situation has not been solved, because I am still cold, in my mind's eye it has been made perfectly understandable, and that is what is important. My mind has invented a god of sorts, a means of putting the world right.

❦❦❦

MAN
THE MYTH MAKER

❦❦❦

Man's remarkable talent for inventing myths is surpassed only by his ability to believe in them. The French philosopher Henri Bergson, who died in 1941, was long fascinated by man's myth-making ability. When you read a particularly moving novel you can be emotionally overwhelmed by it, as you can be by a film. But all the while you know fully well that the people you are reading about or whose images you see on the screen, are not flesh-and-blood beings. Nevertheless, you react as if they were. This is all part of our world of myth, Bergson tells us, and it is an extremely important function of the mind. What would Nature have done, after endowing man with his unique intellectual ability, he asks, if she had wanted to guard against certain dangers of intellectual activity? The chief among such dangers would be any threat to the loss of intelligence itself. A casual look about us supplies the answer, Bergson says.

For example, the finest scientific argument in the world, and one that may go unchallenged for a century, can be brought toppling down in an instant in the light of a new discovery.

Living amid such uncertainty, living with truths that are not eternal but continually subject to change, is a pretty lean intellectual diet for most of us. The mind needs more to feed on. What Bergson is getting at is that we probably would find life unbearable if we depended *only* on our intelligence to make sense out of the world. Nature came to the rescue and prevented intelligence from destroying us by enabling us to respond to a fictional world as if it were real. "Counterfeit experience," Bergson called it. As counterfeit experience masquerading as perception, a persistent dream with vivid images can later prevent us from performing certain acts in the real world, or can be an important reason for our changing a certain plan to act.

Human intelligence came equipped with a kind of safety valve, according to Bergson, that safety valve being superstition: "the ability of intelligence to shut itself off in time of stress and to accept a counterfeit experience in the place of a real one." For that reason, Bergson says, "an intelligent being is naturally superstitious, and intelligent [beings] are the only superstitious beings."

Anyone further interested in man's myth-making faculty should read the Swiss psychologist Carl G. Jung's extensive writings about the human "collective unconscious." Jung viewed the collective unconscious as a distillation of the total experience of mankind that lurks within each of us and is revealed now and again by the symbols that occur in our dreams, as well as in our art.

No culture that we know of is without its myths, fanciful-sounding tales retold through the ages to provide simple explanations of things difficult or impossible to know through direct experience. For example, the origin of the Universe and man's origin. Myths also serve in other ways. They keep the "tribe"

❦ *According to Jung, symbols used by various cultures spring from man's "collective unconscious." An example is the cross motif, here (from left to right) represented by ankh, the Egyptian hieroglyph for "life"; a crosslike sculpture of a Greek fertility goddess (c. 2500 B.C.); the swastika, used by several cultures with various meanings; a fifth- or sixth-century Cornish cross, possibly a sacred stone originally, but later given a cross motif by Christians; the so-called Latin cross, common since Christian times.* SCIENCE PHOTO/GRAPHICS, LTD.

together by providing each and every member with the same counterfeit experience. They may serve in the place of a formal system of laws as rigid guides for social conduct and as embodiments of religion and philosophy. According to the Pueblo Indians, myth enables them to hold to the faith of their ancestors. Ask a Navaho, an Iroquois, an Australian aborigine, or an Eskimo how old their myths are, and you will be told simply that they are *very* old. Even the oldest myths known were extremely old by the time they first were written down. The oldest written records available to us go back more than 5,000 years, but people must have been creating myths at least some quarter of a million years ago. What those original myths were like we shall never know. Even the more recent ones have been hopelessly blurred during the countless retellings by preliterate societies as small adjustments were made here and there to bring the myths "up to date" and so preserve their relevance.

Even though we may never be sure that a given myth we

may be reading is faithful to its original form, chances are that the larger truths it deals with have survived time. The creation myths we will be concerned with in the next chapter are examples.

🏵🏵🏵

INVENTION OF THE GODS

🏵🏵🏵

At the heart of early man's myth-making faculty was the irresistible, childlike urge to attribute human qualities to all of nature. Thinking that other animals have emotions just like our own—hope, fear, love, hate, anger, despair, respect—and that their feelings and actions can be understood on the basis of such emotions is called *anthropomorphism* (meaning "man" + "form"). As any biologist will tell you, it is the greatest barrier to learning about the ways animals behave as they do. It was an anthropomorphic view of nature that primitive man took in his attempts to understand the natural world. And its hangover in modern man is all too evident in the hundreds of young children's books that are mines of misinformation about plants and animals that talk and sing and go about life much as human beings do.

Early man's ignorance of the laws of nature—the *cause* of rain and thunder, the laws of motion and gravitation—caused him to view the world and reason principally from his own personal experiences. And experiences were bound to vary from one person to another. All activity of living and nonliving things alike was seen as regulated by purpose. A stone rolls down a hill because it *wants* to, and birds "sing" because they are *happy*. Each event, whether on land, in the sea, or in the sky, and whether it involved a planet or platypus, could be explained and understood in personal and human terms.

Moon, Sun, and stars, then, appeared or disappeared for the simple reason that they wanted to, for they too possessed a life force, and that life force could be appealed to and its possessor gratified or angered accordingly.

A god had been invented, and there is hardly a culture that we know of that has not elevated both Sun and Moon to the position of gods.

To this day we pay tribute, if only indirectly, to these gods of old as we practice certain religious ceremonial rites. For instance, the Christian Easter and Passover, or Jewish Pesach, both have their origin in heathen rites of ages past. People then worshipped a Sun god and celebrated the spring reawakening of nature at spring equinox, about March 21, after which time the days lengthen and the nights become shorter. The word "Easter" derives from the Norse *Ostara,* or *Eostre,* the Teutonic goddess of dawn. May Day was an age-old event even when Roman youths danced and sang in the fields in honor of Flora, goddess of fruits and flowers.

The origins of such pagan rites tend to become obscured by time. The English, for example, changed the original significance of May Day by dedicating it to their hero Robin Hood and Maid Marian because Robin Hood died on that day. Even so, the tradition of dancing around the maypole continues to this day although its original purpose as nature worship has long been forgotten. Instinctively, man tends to hang onto the symbols of his past even though their meanings have been obscured by the mist of time. All such celebrations and festivals have the momentary effect of stopping passing-time, of unifying all the participants in Great Time.

✤ *The tradition of dancing around the Maypole—here seen in New York City's Central Park in 1905—continues to this day, although its original purpose as nature worship has long been forgotten.*
THE GRANGER COLLECTION

✻✻✻

HOW MYTHS
GIVE FORM
TO THE WORLD

✻✻✻

The Sun, Moon, and planets, the ancients believed, moved because they were inhabited by an intelligence superhuman in power. Such a prescientific model of the world could explain any celestial event, one as regularly recurring as the phases of the Moon or one as uncommon as the appearance of a comet. Influenced by love, greed, lust, hate, fear, jealousy, ambition, and other human passions, the motions of the Sun and other sky objects were easily explained. How many decades or centuries did it take primitive people to detect the yearly pattern in the Sun's apparent motion across the great sky dome? At each successive noon it could be seen to climb progressively higher from December 22 and reach its highest overhead point on June 22. After that its midday position could be seen to become progressively lower until it reached its lowest point again in December. When such a pattern eventually was noticed, it had to be accounted for in some way.

Since primitive man imagined every rock, twig, and star to be inhabited by a life force, it was reasonable to invent tales that served as substitutes for natural causes to account for motions and other observed changes. The Sun's annual apparent motion up and down the sky could be explained quite simply: One day the spirit of the night grew jealous of the great and powerful Sun spirit and tried to convince the people that the Sun was not great and powerful at all but was really a weakling. After all, anyone could see that the Sun was being chased across the sky each day. When the people began to mock the Sun for his weakness, he became angry and said that he would leave them in darkness forever.

At first the people were not alarmed because they believed the night spirit, but then each day the Sun arched lower and lower across the sky. Soon the nights became longer than the days, and it grew cold. Gradually it became so cold that the lakes and rivers froze. At this stage the people did become alarmed and began to do everything they could think of to please the Sun spirit: they offered sacrifices, played music, and danced for his pleasure. Eventually the Sun spirit was won over, for soon he began to climb higher and higher in the sky each day and melted the frozen lakes and rivers and made the days longer than the nights. But to make sure that the people never forgot their lesson, the Sun vowed to remind them each year of their rudeness to him by spending part of the year low in the sky and letting the evil night spirit rule the people for a while. Thereafter, each spring, when the length of the day and the night became the same, at the spring equinox, about March 21—the people rejoiced and celebrated the return of the Sun. This was the pagan rite of spring, the origin of Easter.

For primitive people the changing seasons seem not to have been continuous or related but were separate events. The life forces inhabiting all of nature were imagined to be in perpetual conflict, just as they were in man himself. Summer expressed its power of domination by driving away winter, but there was no assurance that summer would again win the struggle the next time. Each event in nature was new and not necessarily related to what preceded or followed. It is not difficult to imagine the insecurity people must have felt about life. But the same is true of those people today who substitute superstition for reason based on natural causes. Since the wind spirit, the frost spirit, the Sun and Moon, the lightning spirit, and all those other humanized forces of nature acted whimsically, as people often do, then like people those forces had to be appealed to through their emotions.

Many others in addition to Piaget, Bergson, and Jung have tried to uncover what lies at the basis of man's ability and need to create and perpetuate myths. It has been important to touch on their ideas in this chapter in an attempt to pry open that crack into the mind of primitive man in order to gain at least a glimpse of how he may have perceived the world with his mind's eye. But all we have today to go on is the residue of his thinking: hand-me-down, fanciful tales about legendary warriors and monsters and mythical hunters who nightly haunt the heavens as they parade across the sky. We can only be sure that he was *not* looking for an explanation of the world based on natural causes. That is the role of science, at the opposite pole from mythology.

A scientific view of the world, including man as a part of that world, was long in coming. It was to wait some 200,000 years or more until the Golden Age of the Greek philosophers. The myth makers of former ages, troubled by unfamiliar and unexplained events in this mysterious Universe, eased their minds by seeing the world through their myths, which served the triple purpose of entertainment, instruction, and mental pacifier. Because myths veiled certain troubling aspects of reality from man, they saved him from needlessly spinning the wheels of his mind, from racking his brain to solve problems that had no solutions, for a time anyway, problems including his own origin and that of the world.

The British archaeologist Jacquetta Hawkes relates in her book, *The First Great Civilizations,* a haunting account of the burial of a Mesopotamian king and queen:

> Here a king and a queen had been accompanied to the next world not only with all their most precious possessions, the funerary vehicles and the draft animals harnessed to them, but also by scores of richly attired ladies, by soldiers, servitors and grooms. Ladies had been buried holding lyres, their fingers on the strings. All these people of the court seemed to have died readily, peacefully, according to a well established practice.

How thoroughly those people must have accepted that world of counterfeit experience, and how convinced they must have been of its reality.

2

IN THE BEGINNING . . .

ACCORDING TO THE ENUMA ELISH

The search for the blurred dates of creation of the world and of life have long haunted man. One of the oldest known accounts of the creation of the Universe takes us back some 5,000 years and more to the land of the Babylonians between the eastern end of the Mediterranean Sea and the Persian Gulf. Here lie *The Arabian Nights* fable lands of twelve centuries ago, the biblical Garden of Eden, the hanging gardens of Babylon, and the home of Abraham, traditional founder of the Hebrew people.

The creation myth of the Babylonians goes by the formal name of *Enuma Elish*, which means simply "when above," but it is popularly known as the "Babylonian Genesis." As old as the *Enuma Elish* is in its Babylonian form, it can be dated to a still older time when people known as the Sumerians inhabited that region of the Near East before they were conquered by the Babylonians. One of the many reasons for dating the *Enuma Elish* to a time even earlier than that of the Babylonians is the myth's hero role, which calls for a robust god of storm and wind. The chief god of the ancient Babylonians was Marduk, and it was he we find cast in the hero role in the Babylonian version of the *Enuma Elish*. But Marduk was not a stormy figure. The Babylonians, it seems, took over the plot of the *Enuma Elish* from the Sumerians and cast their own and newer gods in the old roles. They did, however, assign a secondary role to Enlil, the chief god of the defeated Sumerians, a wise political move for a victorious group to make in order to pacify the people they had conquered. Enlil *was* a robust god of storm and exactly fits the role of the central figure of the *Enuma Elish*. So it seems virtually certain that the creation myth goes back at least to Sumerian times and quite likely much earlier still, to a time long before writing had been invented.

※※※

CREATION
OF THE WORLD

※※※

In the beginning, according to the *Enuma Elish*, there was only a chaos of water—sweet (fresh) water of the land (represented by the great god Apsu), salt water of the sea (represented by the goddess Ti'amat), and cloudy mists (represented by a third spirit, Mummu). The three kinds of water were at first mingled in a single mass, and there was no sky above nor earth below, only the watery chaos. Eventually, however, the two gods Lahmu and Lahamu were produced from the marriage of Apsu and Ti'amat.

THE CHIEF BABYLONIAN GODS

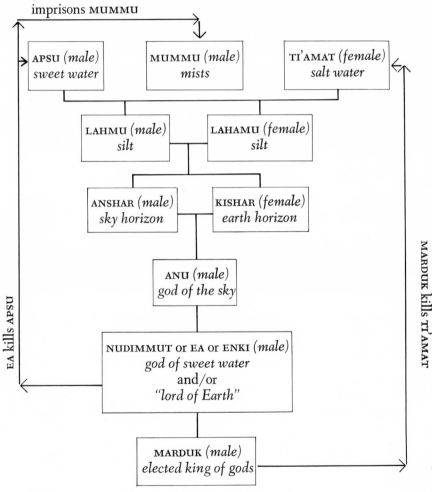

Scholars of the *Enuma Elish* think that Lahmu and Lahamu represented silt, such as that the Sumerians saw carried by the waters of the Tigris and Euphrates rivers. These two gods gave birth to Anshar and Kishar, who represent "the horizon," one a circle enclosing the sky and the other a circle enclosing Earth. Anshar and Kishar gave birth to the sky god Anu, who of himself gave birth to Nudimmut (or Enki), god of the sweet waters. However, Enki, also called Ea, had another aspect, that of a god who ruled Earth. While the sky was created in a round or spherical form in the likeness of Anshar, Earth was created in the form of a disk in the likeness of Anu. Until the time of the early Greeks, most people continued to think of Earth as a disk floating in the world-ocean.

The first lines of the *Enuma Elish* quickly establish the key gods who give form to the world:

When a sky above had not [yet even] been mentioned
[And] the name of firm ground below has not [yet even]
   been thought of;
[When] only primeval Apsu, their begetter,
And Mummu and Ti'amat—she who gave birth to them all—
Were mingling their waters in one;
When no bog had formed [and] no island could be found;
When no god whosoever had appeared,
Had been named by name, had been determined as to [his] lot,
Then were gods formed within them [that is, within Apsu,
   Mummu, and Ti'amat].

So in the Sumerian-Babylonian creation timetable, the first "geological" event to take place was formation of the first world-stuff, or silt. It came from the mingling of the fresh waters and the salt waters and took shape as a huge circle, the horizon, which year by year grew as more and more silt came into being and gave rise first to the sky and then to Earth. Pictured as two huge disks stuck together, the sky and Earth disks eventually were separated by the wind and the region between them somehow inflated into an enormous closed volume of space. The upper surface became the sky, the lower surface the ground, and all was surrounded by the primeval waters of chaos, or the primeval sea out of which all things living and nonliving originated.

The *Enuma Elish* myth goes on at great length describing restlessness and then conflict among the gods and eventually a feeling among them that a new king god must be found. The trouble begins when the lesser gods gather and dance wildly, whereupon the three chief gods, Apsu, Mummu, and Ti'amat, resolve to put down this new boisterous behavior, Apsu saying:

> Abhorrent have become their ways to me,
> I am allowed no rest by day, by night no sleep.
> I will abolish, yea, I will destroy their ways,
> that peace may reign [again] and we may sleep.

Here we see two forces in conflict—the inertia and inactivity of the older generation gods Apsu, Mummu, and Ti'amat as opposed to the new activity and dynamism of the younger generation gods. Progress, we are reminded, is born only out of conflict. The lesser gods are enraged when they hear of Apsu's plan. Ea kills Apsu and then imprisons Mummu, which leaves the powerful Ti'amat still free. How is Ti'amat to be subdued? Neither Ea nor any of the other gods is up to the task of defeating her, it seems. Here is where a new king god must be found, a god powerful in authority and at the same time physically powerful enough to defeat Ti'amat in battle. In short, the old order must be put down by revolution and a new order born out of it.

Here is where the hero figure comes in. In the Sumerian version of the myth, the young god elected by the council of gods was the robust god Enlil, but in the later Babylonian version the Babylonian god Marduk, Ea's son, is made the hero. So Marduk is to be armed and sent into battle against Ti'amat, who represents the universal and all-powerful sea. Meanwhile, the forces of chaos also meet in council and draw up their plans to do battle with the young, upstart gods:

> Angry, scheming, restless day and night,
> they are bent on fighting, rage and prowl like lions.
> Gathered in council, they plan the attack,
> Mother Hubur—creator of all forms—
> adds irresistible weapons, has borne monster serpents,
> sharp toothed, with fang unsparing;
> has filled their bodies with poison for blood.
> Fierce dragons she has draped with terror,
> crowned with flame and made like gods,
> so that whoever looks upon them shall perish with fear.

To make a long myth short, Marduk first defeats the army of the forces of chaos and then must confront Ti'amat, who has assumed the form of a monster. After enclosing her in his net, he commands the wind to hold her powerful jaws open just when she is about to swallow him. He then fires an arrow through her mouth and into her heart. Next he mashes her skull, thoroughly bleeds her, and finally he cuts her body into two pieces. Now here is where the universe is created a *second* time, not an uncommon event in mythology; stories have the habit of recurring in several different versions. As we will find later, man is first created in Genesis I:27, and then in II:7 he is created a second time. And Noah starts life anew in Genesis VIII. Some religious fundamentalists, however, deny that Genesis has two different accounts of creation, maintaining that the second one is simply an elaboration of the first.

Anyway, during the second Babylonian creation, Marduk raises up one half of Ti'amat's body and with it forms the sky. There he establishes his home after making certain that the sea water still filling her hacked-up body will not come cascading out. Earlier Ea had killed Apsu (sweet water) and had made his home on Apsu; so as Earth (Ea) floated on and was surrounded by water, so was the sky in the second creation. Again, we are reminded that a world-ocean surrounded all of creation.

In their attempts to understand the world around them, people during the predawn of science invented answers to questions they were not yet able to cope with in an impersonal, scientific way. They breathed life into the inanimate world about them by inhabiting the soil, sky, wind, and all other natural phenomena with gods driven by human desires and fears but in possession of superhuman powers. Dreaming, fainting, hallucinations, all were expressions of an inner spirit which, when its possessor died, left the body. All things were animated by individual spirits, a belief called "animism." But some things—the Sun, magicians, and priests, for example—had more *mana* (a sort of cosmic electricity) than others and were elevated to higher spiritual positions of regard and worship.

According to the scholar of Sumerian antiquities Thorkild Jacobsen, we can see in the *Enuma Elish* a basic animistic attempt to account for certain events commonly observed by anyone living near the Persian Gulf in ancient Babylonia:

The speculations which here meet us, speculations by which the ancient Mesopotamians thought to penetrate the mystery concealing the origin of the universe, are obviously based upon observation of the way in which new land is actually formed in Mesopotamia. Mesopotamia is an alluvial country. It has been built through thousands of years by silt which has been brought down by the two great rivers, the Euphrates and the Tigris, and has been deposited at their mouths. This process still goes on; and day by day, year by year, the country slowly grows, extending farther out into the Persian Gulf. It is this scene—where the sweet waters of the rivers meet and blend with the salt waters of the sea, while cloud banks hang low over the waters— which has been projected back into the beginning of time. Here still is the primeval watery chaos in which Apsu, the sweet waters, mingles with Ti'amat, the salt waters of the sea; and here the silt—represented by the first of the gods, Lahmu and Lahamu—separates from the water, becomes noticeable, and is deposited.

Jacobsen reminds us that the Babylonians and Sumerians before them turned to myth when they were unable to explain the annual flooding regularly observed in their land. Such flooding has long occurred in such other places as the Nile Valley and elsewhere around the world. With the coming of each seasonal flooding of the Tigris and Euphrates, the Babylonians saw their small world threatened. Possibly it was about to revert to the primeval watery chaos, but it never did. Each year the winds blew and drove the water away, just as they had dried up Ti'amat's blood after she had been hacked to pieces by Marduk.

🌠🌠🌠

CREATION OF LIFE

🌠🌠🌠

In the earlier Sumerian account of how the world began, Enlil, god of the air and ruler of all the world, seizes Ki (Earth) and in the privacy of the clouds fashions out of

THE CHIEF SUMERIAN GODS

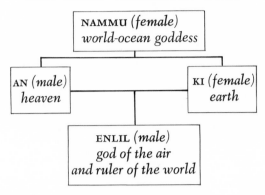

her all living things, the birds, flowers, fishes of the sea, and man. In the later Babylonian account in the *Enuma Elish,* after Marduk has slain Ti'amat he then sets about many tasks of creation. One of the first things he does is set the stage for a calendar by creating the constellations and regulating their periods of apparent rising and setting, as he did for the Sun and Moon. We find an excellent example of how cause and effect are unrelated when Marduk gives instructions to the Moon in her motions:

> At full moon thou shalt face the Sun.
> [But] when the Sun starts gaining on thee in the depth
> of heaven,
> Decrease thy radiance, reverse its growth.

Because the ancients did not understand the motion relationships between Earth, Sun, and Moon or what caused those motions, they had no hope of understanding the real cause of the Moon's change in phases. If they had had such an understanding, Marduk would have said: "When thou shalt face the Sun thy face shall be full," or words to that effect. Today most eighth graders can tell you that at the full, the Moon

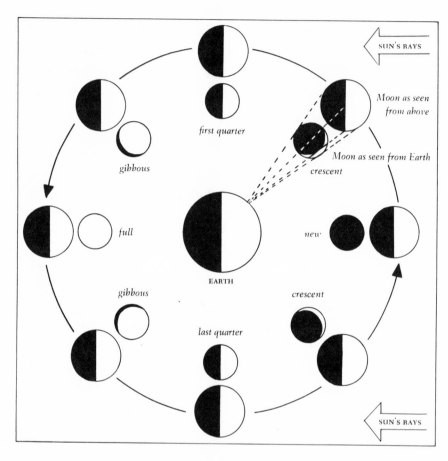

Within the diagram:

SUN'S RAYS

Moon as seen
from above

first quarter

gibbous

Moon as seen from Earth

crescent

full

new

EARTH

gibbous

crescent

last quarter

SUN'S RAYS

✺ *From Earth we see the Moon go through "phases," represented by the inner rim of moons in the diagram. But if you were in space above Earth's North Pole, the Moon would always appear to be half full (outer rim of moons), as would Earth. By studying the dotted-line pattern, shown only for the first cresent phase after new moon, you can understand why an observer on Earth sees the Moon go through phases.* SCIENCE PHOTO/GRAPHICS, LTD.

"faces" the Sun as seen from Earth, when Moon, Earth, and Sun occur in a straight line with Earth in the middle. But endowing her with superhuman powers, Marduk commands the Moon to face the Sun whenever she happens to be shining in full radiance. Actually, of course, the Moon is always facing the Sun. And again, she is ordered to "decrease thy radiance" gradually as she proceeds into last quarter (half moon) about a week later.

Marduk next decides to free the gods of all menial tasks and to transfer those tasks to a newcomer in the world, man, whom Marduk arranges to be created. He begins by assembling all the gods and asking them who incited Ti'amat to wage battle against them. When told that it was Kingu, Ti'amat's second husband, the assembly orders Kingu to be bound and executed. Then under the direction of Marduk's father, Ea, ruler of Earth, man is created:

"I will create Lullu, 'man' be his name,
I will form Lullu, man.
Let him be burdened with the toil of the gods,
   that they may freely breathe." . . .
They bound [Kingu], held him before Ea,
Condemned him, severed his arteries.
And from his blood they formed mankind.
Ea then toil imposed on man and set gods free.

The liberation of the gods takes place, and they are assigned to Anu, god of the sky. As a tribute to Marduk, the gods' final labor is that of building him a magnificent temple in the sacred city of Nippur. The temple is to be a combination banquet and assembly hall to be used by the gods when they are summoned to earth to discuss and rule over the affairs of man. Marduk's place as king of the gods and ruler of the world is assured for

A belief that the Moon, planets, and stars directly control our lives has been common among superstitious people since Babylonian times. In Persian mythology, for instance, the Moon was maleficent and presided over thieves and spies. SCIENCE PHOTO/GRAPHICS, LTD.

eternity, and man is instructed to honor his gods so that the world will continue as an orderly place and people will forever be reminded of the great conquest of order over chaos.

CLASSIFYING CREATION MYTHS

The myths people traditionally have deemed the most important are just those that most contradict our intelligence. These include that large class of myths dealing with creation, which can be grouped into three categories: (1) those in which Earth and its life were fashioned from the parts of some being's body, often a monster; (2) those that have Earth and its life being formed out of a world-ocean; and (3) those in which some supernatural being creates itself and then creates the world *ex nihilo* (out of nothing).

Common to creation myths of all three categories is a setting of stages of opposites: heaven and earth, good and evil, chaos and order, male and female, life and death, inertia and motion, day and night, mortality and immortality, and so on. With the *Enuma Elish* as background, we are now in a better position to appreciate the creation myths of a number of other cultures.

In the beginning there was nothing, according to a Chinese creation myth. Then nothing turned into something, and that something became two parts, one male and the other female. This maleness and femaleness gave rise to another pair of un-identified substances, which in turn produced the creator-god P'an Ku, a grotesque being with horns (the Chinese symbol of supernatural beings), fangs, and a body covered with long hair. His first task as creator was to bring order out of chaos by chiseling the primeval universal substance apart and separating it into sky and land. Next, he sculptured Earth's surface so that it had mountains, valleys, and rivers. He also created the Sun, Moon, and stars. But to complete the scene P'an Ku had to die. His skull provided the perfect dome for the sky; his flesh became Earth's rich soil; his bones turned into the rocks; and the rivers and seas formed from his blood. Trees and all other vegetation grew from his hair. The wind was his breath, thunder his voice, the Moon his right eye and the Sun his left, and his saliva turned into rain. Man was created out of the vermin that covered P'an Ku's body.

There are a number of creation myths in which the creator fashions man out of bits and pieces of his own dead skin. For example, a Bagobo folktale from the Philippines refers to a white god with gold teeth who continually rubbed his skin to keep it white and in the process accumulated a mound of rubbed-off dead skin. Eventually, when the heap was large enough, he made Earth out of it; with the leftover bits he fashioned man. The Pomo Indians of California tell of Madumda, identified simply as an "old man," who scraped dead skin from his body and formed it into a little ball. Then after eight days of sleep he awoke, at which time the little ball had grown and become Earth, whereupon Madumda hurled it off into space. Because the world was so dark, Madumda next created the Sun by blowing a spark from his pipe into the sky. Next he walked around Earth and provided it with its features:

"Here a mountain, here some rocks," he said. "Now a valley, a lake, clover growing, acorns on the mountains, juniper and cherries. There must be potatoes and rabbits," he said, "and on that mountain over there, let there be bear, puma, wolf, coyote, fox, skunk; on this one rattlesnakes, kingsnakes, garter snakes."

On noticing that one side of a mountain was always in shadow, Madumda was disturbed and felt that sometimes it should be lighted. After thinking about the matter for a while, he commanded Earth, "Roll over!" As it slowly turned, that part of the mountain that had been in shadow gradually became bathed in light. It would be interesting to know just how old this creation myth is, since it implies that its inventors presumed, and correctly so, that Earth's rotation on its axis, not a moving Sun, is the cause of day and night.

When he had finished forming Earth's rivers, springs, and mountains and caused trees, bushes, and other plants to grow, Madumda created the people. First he created feathers and then scattered them into the air, whereupon they became bird-people. Out of hairs plucked from his body he created the deer-people, the bear-people, and other four-legged animals. Then out of pieces of dried tendons that he took from a sack and broke into little pieces and scattered over the ground, he created humans. He then called all his people together and said; "This is your land. This is where you will live. There is plenty of food. Eat it." And he left.

In a second part the myth describes Madumda's unhappiness when he returns and finds that the people are fighting each other and otherwise not behaving properly, and how he decides to destroy them by causing a universal flood. He then creates man a second time, but as time passes these people too misbehave and so Madumda destroys them with fire. He destroys a third group of humans by causing an ice age to descend on them. Finally, he creates a fourth group and causes them to speak many different languages, and situates them all over Earth's surface. In this way he thinks he can keep them apart and so prevent their fighting one another. This time the bird-people, the fish-people, and all the others do what they are bid, and Madumda leaves the world for the last time.

This myth is a very close parallel to the Bible stories of the Tower of Babel and the Flood. After the Flood Noah's descendents reach Babylonia and plan to build a tower reaching up to heaven. Disapproving of the idea, Jehovah foils the plan by causing the builders suddenly to begin speaking different languages so that they are unable to understand each other. As the different language groups separated and dispersed over Earth, eventually there evolved diverse racial groups speaking different languages.

Still other creation myths, such as one from the Congo, have the creator in successive fits of vomiting produce first the Sun, Moon, stars, and Earth and then all life upon it. A Scandinavian creation myth tells of Ymir, the first living being, a giant fashioned out of frost. The chief god Odin and his two brothers kill Ymir and make Earth out of his flesh, its oceans out of his blood, the mountains out of his bones, and the trees, grasses, and all other plants out of his hair. Ymir's huge skull forms the sky-dome above, and sparks within his head are scattered as the Sun, Moon, and stars. To this day, his brain broods over Earth as fog and dark rain clouds that hang low, characteristic of certain coastal regions of Scandinavia. At Odin's command, dwarfs that live eternally underground and make beautiful jewels were created out of the maggots in Ymir's dead flesh. Meanwhile the gods made the first man, Ask, out of an ash tree, gave him life, a soul, his five senses, blood, and a power of motion. They likewise fashioned the first woman out of an elm tree and named her Embla.

There are numerous myths that, like the *Enuma Elish*, relate the formation of the world out of a world-ocean. The oldest of the Egyptian creation stories, going back some 6,000 years, says that in the beginning there was nothing but the primeval

THE CHIEF EGYPTIAN GODS

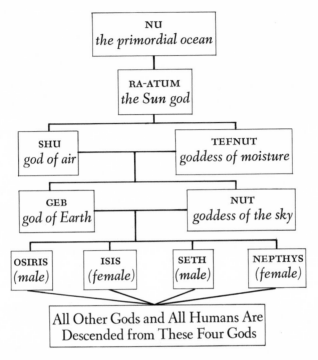

NU
the primordial ocean

RA-ATUM
the Sun god

SHU
god of air

TEFNUT
goddess of moisture

GEB
god of Earth

NUT
goddess of the sky

OSIRIS
(male)

ISIS
(female)

SETH
(male)

NEPTHYS
(female)

All Other Gods and All Humans Are Descended from These Four Gods

ocean, Nun, out of which the first god, the Sun god, created himself. Here, in contrast with some of the myths mentioned earlier, the first being was not produced through the union of a male and a female substance, but out of a sexless world-ocean. Before the Sun god came to rule over all of creation, he was called Atum, which means "everything" and "nothing." But on ruling he became known as Ra-Atum, *Ra* meaning "Sun." On rising up out of the waters of chaos Atum said,

> Out of the abyss I came to be
> But there was no place to stand.

So he created a small mound of earth to support himself, and it became the world.

Next he created Shu, god of the air, and Tefnut, goddess of moisture. From the union of Shu and Tefnut were born Geb, god of Earth, and Nut, goddess of the sky. Notice the parallel here to the Sumerian world-ocean goddess, Nammu, who produced An and Ki, god and goddess of heaven and Earth. Geb and Nut in turn produced the two gods Osiris and Seth and the two goddesses Isis and Nepthys, from whom all the other Egyptian gods, and all men, were descended. Because the Egyptians supposed that gods and men alike were given life from the same source, they did not make a sharp distinction between them.

In other versions of the myth, Ra-Amon, a combination wind-sun god, is cast in the role of creator, as are Ptah and Khnum in still other versions. Although the creator-god represents a different life force in each version, the story each myth tells is essentially the same: the Sun plays the central role of creator, an idea that turns up time and again in myths from all parts of the world invented by peoples who have never had contact with each other to this day. Like the Sumerian myth makers, the Egyptians based their tale on what they could observe to be happening. Each year as the snows melted off the mountains in Ethiopia, the Egyptian segment of the Nile overflowed its banks from about July to October and flooded the surrounding land. After the flood waters had subsided, the silt carried seaward by the river's water was left heaped up in little mounds: a re-creation of the small primeval mound of earth which Atum had created on rising up out of the world-ocean. On examining these small hillocks of slimy mud, a variety of living organisms would be seen thriving under the hot Sun. Here, then, was the original source of the world, quite likely "discovered" independently at different times and in different places by two great prehistoric civilizations.

The following creation myth will serve as a further example of how cultures far removed from each other in space and time can draw essentially the same conclusions from similar observations and weave them into fanciful tales. Myths, it would seem, are a blend of observations of what actually took place and what "should have taken place." The similarity of this creation myth told by the Yuchi Indians of eastern Tennessee to the Egyptian account of the origin of life will be obvious:

In the beginning there was only water. And Someone said, "Who will make the land?"

"I will make the land," said Crawfish. And he dived down to the bottom of that great sea and stirred up the mud with his eight legs and his tail. And he took the mud in his fingers and made a little pile.

The owners of the mud down there said, "Who is stirring up the mud?" And they watched to see. But Crawfish kept stirring up the mud with his tail so that they could not see.

Every day Crawfish dived into the deep water and got a little more mud and put it on the pile. Day by day he piled it up. At last one day as he piled the mud on top of the pile, his hands came out of the water into the air! At last the land appeared above the water.

It was very soft, for it was mud.

Someone said, "Who will stretch out the land? Who will make it hard? Who will make it dry?"

Buzzard stretched out the earth and dried it. He spread his long wings and stretched it. He sailed over the earth; he spread it wide and dried it. Then, tiring, he had to flap his wings and this made the mountains and valleys.

Someone said, "Who will make the light?"

Star said, "I will make light." But it was not enough.

It was said, "Who will make more light?"

"I will make light," said Moon. But it was still night.

Someone said, "More light."

Sun said, "I will make light. I am the mother."

So Sun moved over into the east, and all at once a great beautiful light spread over the world. And then as Sun moved from east to west, a drop of her blood fell and sank into the earth. From this blood and this earth came forth the first people, the Yuchi Indians. They called themselves *Tsohaya,* People of the Sun, and every man who took this name had a picture of the Sun on his door.

Before the Christian era people living in Armenia (now part of the U.S.S.R.) worshiped the Sun god Aramazd, in Persia known as Ahura Mazda. Today a few pagan Armenians worship a Sun god, Areg, and are called "Children of the Sun."

One could relate many, many more creation myths in which a world-ocean or the hacked-up body of a monster form the basis for the genesis of life and the physical Universe, but there is no need. We have not even mentioned the creation accounts in Greek mythology, but to do so would simply take us back to more detailed accounts of Babylonian creationism in which Marduk figures so prominently.

As our brief sampling of creation myths has shown, many such myths are based on people's observation of the silt carried and deposited by the rivers during annual flooding in major river valleys. To early man, these small mounds of earth appeared as if by magic; he had no notion that the life-bearing mud which so interested him originated miles upriver, far from where it was deposited in the river delta. And he had no way of knowing that life did not spring spontaneously from those small earth mounds once they were deposited and warmed by the sun. At that time people didn't realize that life arose in those mounds of mud from living things already there in the form of minute eggs and seeds. In the absence of such knowledge

it was natural to suppose that the Sun-creator each year re-
enacted his original role as he had done during the first beginning.

❀❀❀

ACCORDING
TO THE JUDEO-CHRISTIAN
TRADITION

❀❀❀

In the Judeo-Christian tradition, God the Creator is
all-powerful, all-seeing, and all-knowing. Unlike the creator-
gods in the *Enuma Elish,* the one God of the Jewish and
Christian faiths is indestructible and eternal. He created *ex
nihilo* the very chaos out of which an orderly Universe was
to be fashioned. In II Maccabees it is stated "I beseech thee,
my son, look upon the heaven and the earth, and all that is
therein, and consider that God made them of things that were
not; and so was mankind made likewise."

The biblical creation story as related in the first chapter of
Genesis, which originated some time around 500 B.C., begins
in a way that will sound familar to those who have read selections from the *Enuma Elish,* the Egyptian, and other creation
myths in which the chaos out of which the creator is to fashion
the Universe is a world-ocean. According to Genesis I, God
creates the Universe, Earth and all of its life in six twenty-
four-hour days.

As you read the following two accounts of the creation—both
based on the old Judean "narratives"—notice that in the more
recent version (Genesis I) the diety is called "God." But in the
older account (Genesis II) the deity is called "Lord God," para-
phrased from the Hebrew deity Yahweh, or Jehovah.

✳✳✳

CREATION
OF THE WORLD
AND LIFE

✳✳✳

THE FIRST DAY

1. In the beginning God created the heaven and the earth.

2. And the earth was without form, and void; and darkness was upon the face of the deep: and the Spirit of God moved upon the face of the waters.

3. And God said, Let there be light: and there was light.

4. And God saw the light, that *it was* good: and God divided the light from the darkness.

5. And God called the light Day, and the darkness he called Night. And the evening and the morning were the first day.

THE SECOND DAY

6. And God said, Let there be a firmament [the vault of heaven] in the midst of the waters, and let it divide the waters from the waters.

7. And God made the firmament, and divided the waters which were under the firmament from the waters which were above the firmament: and it was so.

8. And God called the firmament Heaven. And the evening and the morning were the second day.

Notice the close parallel here with the *Enuma Elish* when Marduk slays Ti'amat (the world-ocean), one part of her dragon body becoming the sky, and the earth below also being supported by part of that same world-ocean.

THE THIRD DAY

9. And God said, Let the waters under the heaven be gathered

together unto one place, and let the dry *land* appear: and it was so.

10. And God called the dry *land* Earth, and the gathering together of the waters called he Seas: and God saw that *it was* good.

✻ 11. And God said, Let the Earth bring forth grass, the herb yielding seed, *and* the fruit-tree yielding fruit after his kind, whose seed *is* in itself, upon the earth: and it was so.

✻ 12. And the Earth brought forth grass *and* herb yielding seed after his kind, and the tree yielding fruit, whose seed *was* in itself, after his kind: and God saw that *it was* good.

13. And the evening and the morning were the third day.

THE FOURTH DAY

14. And God said, Let there be lights in the firmament of the heaven, to divide the day from the night: and let them be for signs and for seasons, and for days, and years:

15. And let them be for lights in the firmament of the heaven, to give light upon the earth: and it was so.

16. And God made two great lights; the greater light to rule the day, and the lesser light to rule the night: *he made* the stars also.

17. And God set them in the firmament of the heaven, to give light upon the earth.

18. And to rule over the day and over the night, and to divide the light from the darkness: and God saw that *it was* good.

19. And the evening and the morning were the fourth day.

It is interesting that light and darkness, day and night, and morning and evening were created on the first day, but it is not until the fourth day that the Sun, Moon, and stars were created. One of the first things God does is to create a calendar or the means of developing one—lights for the seasons, days, and years. When primitive peoples learned to change from hunting and food gathering to the cultivation of crops, it was extremely important that they have a means of reckoning time in order to know the most advantageous times to plant. In Babylonian, Egyptian, and other cultures the high priests were the calendar keepers. The simple people stood in awe of the priests for their ability to forecast the seasons. An ability to forecast an event—the coming of spring, the seasonal flood waters, or an eclipse—was regarded as an ability to *cause* the event. So until the common people learned some basic astronomy the calendar was regarded as sacred and magical.

Also on the fourth day God created "lights in the firmament of heaven *to give light upon the earth.*" Here the implication is that the rest of the Universe is being fashioned for the benefit of Earth, Earth presumably being the most important place in God's creation. And later, when God creates man, man becomes the greatest of God's acts of creation, His masterwork, and God gives man all of Earth to rule over. So not only is the notion of Earth as the focal point of the Universe emphasized, but it is made clear that of all things on Earth man is the most important and that all living things are intended for man's use, to "subdue" and have "dominion" over, as God willed on the sixth day. This view of man as the central and most "important" figure in God's Universe for many centuries prevented man from seeing himself as an integral part of nature; instead he regarded himself as a very special creature apart from nature.

The Greek scholar Socrates (about 400 B.C.) reportedly marveled at ". . . the care the gods have taken to furnish man with what he needs [and] . . . how they make the earth to yield it [and]/. . minister not only to our wants but to our enjoyment." Not until the 1800s was Charles Darwin once and for all to bury the notion that nature exists to serve man.

THE FIFTH DAY

20. And God said, Let the waters bring forth abundantly the moving creatures that hath life, and fowl *that* may fly above the earth in the open firmament of heaven.

21. And God created great whales, and every living creature that moveth, which the waters brought forth abundantly, after their kind, and every winged fowl after his kind: and God saw that *it was* good.

22. And God blessed them, saying Be fruitful, and multiply, and fill the waters in the seas; and let fowl multiply in the earth.

23. And the evening and the morning were the fifth day.

THE SIXTH DAY

✳ 24. And God said, Let the earth bring forth the living creature after his kind, cattle, and creeping thing, and beast of the earth after his kind: and it was so.

25. And God made the beast of the earth after his kind, and cattle after their kind, and every thing that creepeth upon the earth after his kind: and God saw that *it was* good.

26. And God said, Let us make man in our image, after our likeness; and let them have dominion over the fish of the sea, and over the fowl of the air, and over the cattle, and over all the earth, and over every creeping thing that creepeth upon the earth.

27. So God created man in his *own* image; and in the image of God created he him; male and female created he them.

28. And God blessed them, and God said unto them, Be fruitful, and multiply, and replenish the earth, and subdue it: and have dominion over the fish of the sea, and over the fowl of the air, and over every living thing that moveth upon the earth.

29. And God said, Behold, I have given you every herb bearing seed, which is upon the face of all the earth, and every tree, in the which *is* the fruit of a tree yielding seed; to you it shall be for meat.

30. And to every beast of the earth, and to every fowl of the air, and to every thing that creepeth upon the earth, wherein *there is* life, *I have given* every green herb for meat: and it was so.

31. And God saw every thing that he had made, and behold, *it was* very good. And the evening and the morning were the sixth day.

And so ends the first chapter of Genesis.

Although God commands the first man and woman, "Be fruitful, and multiply, and replenish the earth," he does not advise them how to avoid the inevitable problem of sisters marrying brothers and bearing children, a situation leading to all kinds of genetic difficulties.

In Chapter II of Genesis, which originated about 350 years earlier than Chapter I, again we are told how God created man. This was in the year 4004 B.C., according to James Ussher, Archbishop of Armagh, Ireland, who from 1650 to 1654 drew up a timetable of events described in the Bible.

5. . . . The Lord God had not caused it to rain upon the earth, and *there was* not a man to till the ground.

6. But there went up a mist from the earth, and watered the whole face of the ground.

7. And the Lord God formed man *of* the dust of the ground and breathed into his nostrils the breath of life; and man became a living soul.

8. And the Lord God planted a garden eastward in Eden; and there he put the man whom he had formed.

9. And out of the ground made the Lord God to grow every tree that is pleasant to the sight, and good for food; and the tree of life also in the midst of the garden, and the tree of knowledge of good and evil. . . .

15. And the Lord God took the man, and put him into the garden of Eden, to dress it and to keep it.

16. And the Lord God commanded the man, saying, Of every tree of the garden thou mayest freely eat:

17. But of the tree of knowledge of good and evil, thou shalt not eat of it: for in the day that thou eatest thereof thou shalt surely die.

18. And the Lord God said, *It is* not good that the man should be alone: I will make him an help meet for him.

19. And out of the ground the Lord God formed every beast of the field, and every fowl of the air, and brought *them* unto Adam, to see what he would call them; and whatsoever Adam called every living creature, that *was* the name thereof.

20. And Adam gave names to all cattle, and to the fowl of the air, and to every beast of the field: but for Adam there was not found an help meet for him.

21. And the Lord God caused a deep sleep to fall upon Adam, and he slept; and he took one of his ribs, and closed up the flesh instead thereof.

22. And the rib, which the Lord God had taken from man, made he a woman, and brought her unto the man.

23. And Adam said, This *is* now bone of my bones, flesh of my flesh: she shall be called Woman, because she was taken out of man.

Through Adam, God also created language. The belief that language was given to man by the gods is found in several other religions as well. The ancient Egyptians believed that writing was given to them by Thoth, their god of wisdom. *Ndw-ntr,* meaning "the speech of gods," is the Egyptian word for writing. The Mayas of Middle America believed that their god, Itzamna, gave them writing. In Japanese *kami no moji* (meaning "divine characters") is the name for the lost prehistoric written language of Japan. Hindu and Buddhist writings would have us believe that at one time all people spoke a common language, presumably god-given. Unhappily, every search for an *Ursprache* (*ur* means primitive; *sprache* means language) or one root language from which all other languages arose has failed.

In Chapter IV of Genesis, Adam and Eve have two sons, Cain and Abel. Cain grows jealous of Abel and kills him. God punishes Cain by making him "a fugitive and a vagabond." The next thing we learn in Chapter IV is that Cain is married, produces a son, Enoch, and builds a city (in the year 3375 B.C.). And just as mysteriously, Enoch finds a wife, as does his offspring. Adam and Eve then have a third son, Seth, who also finds a wife, and Seth produces a son named Enos, which ends Chapter IV. In Chapter V, however, the apparent mystery of the wives suddenly appearing in Chapter IV is cleared up when we are told that Adam lived for 930 years, during which time he produced sons and daughters; Seth lived for 912 years and also produced sons and daughters. Chapter V ends with the death of Noah's father, Lamech, at the age of 777, at which time Noah was about 500 years old. The time is 2448 B.C.

The two genealogies found in Chapter IV and Chapter V of Genesis "differ in vocabulary, style, and outlook," according to the biblical scholar John M. Groton. Chapter V is in the style of and associated with Chapter I, while Chapter IV is in the style of and associated with the older Chapter II.

⁂

THE UNIVERSAL FLOOD

⁂

The Pomo Indian creation-god Madumda, on visiting man after having created him, was disheartened and angry because man was not behaving himself, whereupon Madumda caused a great flood that washed man away. Many creation myths from many different cultures have accounts of a world-wide flood. One of the oldest we know of is about a legendary Sumerian king named Gilgamesh who tries to achieve immortality so that he may be a better ruler of his people. As a child, Gilgamesh had heard the story of a king who also wanted eternal life. One day the gods sent a great flood over the earth by commanding it to rain for six days and six nights. However, the god of wisdom had warned the king to build a great ship and to bring into it one pair of all the animals of creation. He did, and on the seventh day the great storm ceased, and the Sun broke through the clouds, but all the king could see about him was water. So at first he sent out a dove to find land, but the dove failed to return. Next he sent a swallow, but the swallow also failed to return. Next he sent a raven, who also failed to return. Finally, the boat drifted to land on the mountain of Nizir. Here the good king in his gratitude made sacrifices to the gods and was justly rewarded with immortality for carrying out their wishes.

In Chapter VI of Genesis we find that around 2350 B.C., when Noah was about 600 years old:

> 5. God saw that the wickedness of man *was* great in the earth, and *that* every imagination of the thoughts of his heart *was* only evil continually.
>
> 6. And it repented the Lord that he had made man on the earth and it grieved him at his heart.
>
> 7. And the Lord said, I will destroy man, whom I have created, from the face of the earth; both man and beast, and the creeping thing, and the fowls of the air: for it repenteth me that I have made them.

Noah, being a just man, had won God's favor and was told:

> 14. Make thee an ark of gopher-wood: rooms shalt thou make

in the ark, and shalt pitch it within and without with pitch.

15. And this *is the fashion* which thou shalt make it of: the length of the ark *shall be* 300 cubits [1 cubit is about 20 inches], the breadth of it 50 cubits, and the height of it 30 cubits.

16. A window shalt thou make to the ark, and in a cubit shalt thou finish it above; and the door of the ark shalt thou set in the side thereof: *with* lower, second, and third *stories* shalt thou make it.

17. And, behold, I, even I, do bring a flood of waters upon the earth, to destroy all flesh, wherein *is* the breath of life, from under heaven; *and* every thing that *is* in the earth shall die.

18. But with thee will I establish my covenant: and thou shalt come into the ark; thou, and thy sons, and thy wife, and thy sons' wives with thee.

19. And of every living thing of all flesh, two of every *sort* shalt thou bring into the ark, to keep *them* alive with thee: they shall be male and female. . . .

22. Thus did Noah; according to all that God commanded him, so did he.

Again, two versions of the flood are combined in the biblical account. In the more recent version, given in Chapter VI and associated with Chapter I of Genesis, one pair of every species is to be brought into the ark. But in the Chapter VII version, associated with the older Chapter II, we find:

2. Of every clean beast thou shalt take to thee by sevens, the male and his female; and of beasts that *are* not clean by two, the male and his female.

The great flood lasted 150 days, we are told, after which just as a wind blew away the blood of Ti'amat in the *Enuma Elish* myth, God caused a wind to blow and dry up the flood waters (Chapter VIII):

"God made a wind to pass over the earth, and the waters assuaged." The ark comes to shore on Mount Ararat and Noah sends out first a raven and then a dove to learn if the receding waters have yet exposed the land. God tells Noah to leave the ark and take all the animals with him, and mankind is given a third beginning, as the Lord says:

17. Bring forth with thee every living thing that *is* with thee, of all flesh, *both* of fowl, and of cattle, and of every creeping thing that creepeth upon the earth; that they may breed abundantly in the earth, and be fruitful, and multiply upon the earth.

And, as in the Gilgamesh legend, Noah builds an altar to God and "offer[s] burnt-offerings on the altar."

21. And the Lord smelled a sweet savour: and the Lord said in his heart, I will not again curse the ground any more for man's sake; for the imagination of man's heart *is* evil from his youth: neither will I again smite any more every thing living as I have done.

In short, man is promised eternal life, as was the king upon offering sacrifices in the Gilgamesh legend.

As we read the book of Genesis, beginning with the story of the creation, progressing to the end, and reliving those accounts which the Hebrews took over from the Babylonians, we eventually reach the time of Abraham and Moses. Here, finally, are flesh-and-blood human beings we can identify with. It is as though we had begun the journey in a dream inhabited by unreal beings and unreal events, but gradually we awaken into the world of reality. As we do, the dream solidifies into something real, and suddenly we find ourselves a part of history.

So far in this book our concern with the origin of the Universe and of the diverse living forms inhabiting at least one of its planets has been from a supernatural point of view: the age-old assumption that a divine creator brought order out of chaos in some timeless past. For as long as people viewed nature as being inhabited and manipulated by an endless variety of spirits, it was impossible to look for natural causes that set the world in motion and kept it running. Until an alternative point of view to the supernatural presented itself, people could not reframe their questions about the origins of the Universe and life.

Our concern here is not with the "truthfulness" of the various accounts of creation we have been considering. Each has a kind of truth that is beyond the verifiable, beyond the need of proof. Nor is our concern the importance of the role that myths play in religion. The fact is that many people believe every single word of the Bible to be literally true, but others look on the biblical version of the creation as allegory. To say that one group is "right" and the other "wrong" accomplishes nothing. Our *beliefs* are private affairs mysteriously fashioned in the secret recesses of our minds, and to feel compelled to defend them is to suggest that they are vulnerable, a condition we are reluctant to admit.

❁❁❁

BREAKING
WITH THE PAST

❁❁❁

Earlier in this chapter we said that primitive people found many aspects of their world impossible to understand—the Moon's and Sun's apparent passage overhead, the planets' motions against the background of stars, the germination of seeds, lightning, meteors, and so on. In an age before science

✼ *This ancient stone carving is one of many from Egyptian mythology showing the creation of life on Earth. Here Nut, goddess of the sky, is arched over Geb, god of Earth. The union of Nut and Geb gave rise to all other Egyptian gods and humans.*

could help them understand the natural causes of these and many other equally perplexing events, supernatural causes offered, if not enlightenment, at least a certain peace of mind. In the language of science today, we would say that in his invention of myths man had begun to develop a model that successfully explained what he could observe of and in the Universe. So long as the model worked, fine, but there was bound to come a time when it began to fail.

Exactly when the model began to break down is hard to say. It did not happen overnight. Surely there were skeptics among the old Babylonians, individuals who saw through the old myths and asked what actually made the Moon go through phases, who refused to cover their heads during an eclipse, and who shunned the astrological hocus-pocus of the astronomer-priests. But the masses held to the old myths and their attendant superstitions, as evident in the widespread belief in astral religion. It was astral religion, a fear of and reverence for the planets and stars, that had spawned astrology. But gradually there emerged a group of thinkers who made a bold break with the past, who threw aside the tarnished gods and the idols of clay that for so long had been unquestioningly worshiped. During the age when these people flourished—the Golden Age of Greece—the astronomer-priests and magicians were gradually finding their positions of authority challenged. The challenge came from this new breed of men who were looking for natural causes for earthquakes, lightning, the size and shape of the Universe, and, particularly, for man's place in it.

3

FROM MYTHS
TO ATOMS

*In different epochs and at different stages of
cultural development the question of the origin
of life has been answered in different ways. This
problem has however always been the focus of a
bitter conflict of ideas between two irreconcilable
schools of philosophy—the conflict between ideal-
ism and materialism.*

—A. I. Oparin (1938)

The break with the old myth systems accounting for
the origin of the Universe and life was not swift. It was a
painfully slow process and in many ways incomplete. It happened in classical Greece, around 600 B.C., about 100 years
before the first chapter of the book of Genesis was to be written.
Philosophers began looking for natural causes for the things
they could observe happening around them. But the masses
of people still clung to the old myths, which had every nook
and cranny and every planet and star inhabited by supernatural
forces with which the destinies of all people were entwined.

The Greek religion and its accompanying mythologies were

terribly disorganized and complex, a house of mirrors made up of bits and pieces from Crete, Egypt, Palestine, Phrygia, Babylonia, and elsewhere. Yet it was out of this background of superstitions that the early Greek philosophers emerged and began to regard the formation of the world and its life as an entirely natural event. These men were to lay the foundation stones of modern science.

※※※

SEARCHING FOR THE "WORLD-STUFF"

※※※

One of the first questions they asked concerned the nature of the matter of which the Universe is composed. What was the *world-stuff?* Thales, who was born around 650 B.C., imagined the single "element" of which all other things were made as water, and he supposed that Earth floated on water. This notion was not necessarily based on the old myths, of which he most certainly was aware, but was more likely based on the then limited observations of the Mediterranean and its surrounding lands. The age of exploration had not yet begun. The great outer sea, that part of the Atlantic Ocean beyond the Pillars of Hercules (the Strait of Gibralter) had not yet been explored, nor had Hanno yet made his historic voyage partway down the west coast of Africa (in 470 B.C.). So it did not seem farfetched to assume that the ocean visible through the Pillars of Hercules extended infinitely into space. Water seemed to be everywhere in the forms of mist, rain, clouds, and steam from a boiling kettle. Thales supposed, as did the writers of the *Enuma Elish,* that water-substance changed into earth-substance. One of Thales's students was Anaximander (about 546 B.C.), who described the world-stuff as an "indefinite something" which shows itself as pairs of opposites. The combining and recombining of hot and cold or wet and dry and of other such paired opposites accounted for the substances fire, water, and earth. Anaximander imagined Earth as being the first solid object in the Universe. Surrounding Earth was a cloak of air-substance, which in turn was surrounded by a sphere of flame-substance. The sphere of flame eventually developed into a system of fiery rings out of which the stars and other celestial bodies were formed. When a resulting gap between Earth and the newly formed stars occurred, there was a separation of Heaven from Earth, which begins to sound like the old creation myths. In Anaximander's scheme of things the stars and other celestial objects were not completed until they received from Earth "exhalations of the moist element." He further tells us that "living creatures arose from the moist element, as it was evaporated by the Sun." The first living things on Earth were trees and other plants, as in the first chapter of Genesis.

Because humans require such a long period of parental care before they learn to care for themselves, Anaximander observed, they could not have come into being as did the other animals. "Hence, had [man] been originally as he is now, he would never have survived. . . . At first human beings arose in the inside of fishes, and after having been reared [that way for some time and becoming] capable of protecting themselves, they were finally cast ashore and took to land." The sequence of Anaximander's account of the origin of Earth and its plant and animal life is very nearly the same as that in the first chapter of Genesis. And true to all the Greek accounts of the creation, in Genesis Earth is formed ahead of the stars and other celestial objects. It is interesting that the first chapter of Genesis was written about 50 years after Anaximander's time.

Anaximenes, who lived between about 600 B.C., and 525 B.C., believed, as did Thales, that all matter was made of a single substance, *pneuma*, or "breath." This breath, a kind of air-vapor, he said, is the substance of all things. From breath, he wrote, come all "the things that are and have been and shall be." Air, he also wrote, "becomes fire. Winds on the other hand are condensed Air. Cloud is formed from Air . . . and Cloud still further condensed becomes water. Water condensed still more turns to earth, and when condensed as much as it can be [it turns into] stones." For a while, the views of Anaximenes were regarded as the high point of all previous thinking.

Around 500 B.C. Heraclitus saw the world as being made up of the single substance fire. "The world," he wrote, " . . . was ever, is now, and shall be an ever-living Fire, with measures of it kindling and measures going out. All things are an exchange for Fire, and Fire for all things." The matter composing all things, according to Heraclitus, is continually changing, so that nothing remains the same. Only change itself was permanent. Because this idea of continual change seemed cheerless to people, Heraclitus became popularly known as the "weeping philosopher." Like Anaximenes, he was searching for a unity of substance.

Around 450 B.C., Empedocles—philosopher, poet, seer, physicist, physician, and social reformer—reintroduced the notion of multiple elements, envisioning the four "root" elements—earth, air, fire, and water. They could be united in various combinations to form complex substances and then separated into their pure forms again. The uniting force was "love" and the force of separation was "strife." Empedocles believed his four root elements to be eternal and unchanging. Nothing has substance of its own, he said, only a mingling and interchange of earth, air, fire, and water. The idea of four elements led to

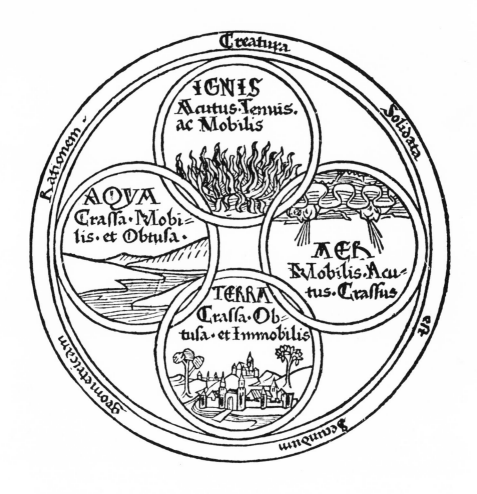

✻ *The four elements of Empedocles: earth, air, fire, and water, from* De Natura Rerum, *dated 1472.*

the idea of the four physical qualities—cold, wet, hot, and dry. Any of the two qualities when joined would produce an element. For example, wet and cold combined to produce water. Wet and hot made air. Hot and dry made fire, and dry and cold made earth. The bones of animals were supposed to be made of one-half fire, one-quarter earth, and one-quarter water. Empedocles's model of the world-stuff caught on among the rationalists. Once blessed with the approval of Aristotle about a century later, the idea, in all its falsity, was given an honored position in science for the next 2,000 years. Not until the year 1661 did the English chemist Robert Boyle provide us with our present-day notion of the chemical elements. Had Aristotle adopted the idea of another of the Greek thinkers who lived around the same time Empedocles did, a rather different view of elements and the atoms of which they are composed would have been introduced sooner.

The first atomist was Democritus (around 450 B.C.), but the atoms of Democritus should not be confused with the atoms we envision today. The major part of Democritus's atomic theory came from his teacher, Leucippus. It held that all matter is made of atoms, which are the smallest things that exist and which cannot be cut in two (the word came from *a*, meaning "not," and *tomé*, meaning "to cut" or "to separate"). The atoms of Democritus were hard and solid, came in many sizes, were in continual motion, and were ageless, which suggested a Universe infinite in time.

The world began, according to Democritus, when atoms quite by chance began bumping into one another, whereupon they stuck together and formed matter. Heavy objects such as rocks and metal supposedly were made of heavy atoms, while fire and air were made of extremely light atoms. Atoms making up water were slick and smooth so they moved over each other easily, but atoms of metal were rough so they clung

together. The ideas of Democritus grated against the old superstitions and therefore were not welcomed. The old ideas about
the Universe and life were all bound up in a straitjacket of
purpose. Things were spoken of principally in terms of the
purposes they served: The Moon exists for the purpose of light-
ing the way by night, the Sun by day. Squirrels have claws
for the purpose of climbing trees. The new rationalists boldly
denied that there was a purpose for the existence of anything
in the Universe. Their chief interest was in the natural composition, structure, and function of all things. Because they
took this "cold and impersonal" view of nature, they became
known as materialists.

Today at the opposite extreme are the creationists, those
who believe that the Bible is a divinely inspired account of how
Earth and its varied life came to be and that every word of the
Bible is literally true. According to the late George Sarton,
historian of science, Democritus's atomic theory excited men's
thinking for centuries. But unhappily it did not seem to confirm
what the Scriptures said about the creation of Earth. For this
reason, wrote Sarton, the theory "was driven underground by
Jewish and Christian teachers, but it never died. The account
of its [changes through the ages] is one of the most remarkable
in the history of knowledge."

"ON THE NATURE
OF THINGS"

The Roman poet-philosopher Lucretius, who lived
during the time Julius Caesar was emperor of Rome (around
50 B.C.), had one major goal in life: to rid people's minds
of the fears spread by superstition and the fear of death. Lu-

cretius has been described as the "poet of science." In his long poem, *On the Nature of Things*, which he wrote for his patron Memmius, he looks not to the old myths to explain natural events, but to natural causes. And all such natural causes, he believed, are traceable to the atoms of Democritus.

Always the rationalist, Lucretius speaks to us in terms that ring of modern thought when he talks of the indestructibility of matter and of biological change. He is quoted at some length here because his thoughts are an attempt to free people from superstition so they could see the world for what it is rather than for what it was supposed to be like. Although some of Lucretius's ideas are original, nearly his entire outlook on life was based on the atomic theory of Democritus as elaborated on by the influential Greek philospoher Epicurus, who lived around 300 B.C.

I will reveal those *atoms* from which nature creates all things and increases and feeds them and into which, when they perish, nature again resolves them. To these in my discourse I commonly give such names as the "raw material," or "generative bodies" or "seeds" of things. Or I may call them "primary particles," because they come first and everything else is composed of them.

When human life lay grovelling in all men's sight, crushed to the earth under the dead weight of superstition whose grim features loured menacingly upon mortals from the four quarters of the sky, a man of Greece was first to raise mortal eyes in defiance, first to stand erect and brave the challenge. Fables of the gods did not crush him, nor the lightning flash and the growling menace of the sky. Rather, they quickened his manhood, so that he, first of vigour of his mind prevailed. He ventured far out beyond the flaming ramparts of the world and voyaged in mind throughout infinity. Returning victorious, he proclaimed to us what can be and what cannot: how a limit is fixed to the power of everything and an immovable frontier post. Therefore superstition in its turn lies crushed beneath his feet, and we by his triumph are lifted level with the skies.

One thing that worries me is the fear that you may fancy yourself embarking on an impious course, setting your feet on the path of sin. Far from it. More often it is this very superstition that is the mother of sinful and impious deeds. . . .

Our starting point will be his principle: *Nothing can ever be created by divine power out of nothing.* The reason why all mortals are so gripped by fear is that they see all sorts of things happening on the earth and in the sky with no discernible cause, and these they attribute to the will of a god. Accordingly, when we have seen that nothing can be created out of nothing, we shall then have a clearer picture of the path ahead, the problem of how things are created and occasioned without the aid of the gods.

First then, if things were made out of nothing, any species could spring from any source and nothing would require seed. Men could rise from the sea and scaly fish from the earth, and birds could be hatched out of the sky. Cattle and other domestic animals and every kind of wild beast, multiplying indiscriminately, would occupy cultivated and waste lands alike. The same fruits would not grow constantly on the same trees, but they would keep changing: any tree might bear any fruit. If each species were not composed of its own generative bodies, why should each be born always of the same kind of mother? Actually, since each is formed out of specific seeds, it is born and emerges into the sunlit world only from a place where there exists the right material, the right kind of atoms. This is why everything cannot be born of everything, but a specific power of generation inheres in specific objects. . . .

The second great principle is this: *Nature resolves everything into its component atoms and never reduces anything to nothing.* If anything were perishable in all its parts, anything might perish all of a sudden and vanish from sight. . . . All objects would regularly be destroyed by the same force and the same cause, were it not that they are sustained by imperishable matter more or less tightly fastened together. Why, a mere touch would be enough to bring about destruction supposing there were no imperishable bodies whose union could be dissolved only by the appropriate force. Actually, because the fastenings of the atoms are of various kinds while their matter is imperishable, compound objects remain intact until one of them encounters a force that proves strong enough to break up its particular constitution. Therefore nothing returns to nothing, but everything is resolved into its constituent bodies. . . . Visible objects therefore do not perish utterly, since nature repairs one thing from another.

I have taught you that things cannot be created out of nothing nor, once born, be summoned back to nothing. Perhaps, however, you are becoming mistrustful of my words, because these atoms of mine are not visible to the eye. Consider, therefore, this further evidence of *bodies whose existence you must acknowledge though they cannot be seen*. First, wind, when its force is roused, whips up waves, founders tall ships and scatters cloud-rack. Sometimes scouring plains with hurricane force it strews them with huge trees and batters mountain peaks with blasts that hew down forests. Such is wind in its fury, when it whoops aloud with a mad menace in its shouting. Without question, therefore, there must be invisible particles of wind which sweep sea and land and the clouds in the sky, swooping upon them and whirling them along in a headlong hurricane.

Lucretius also cites odors, heat, and cold as examples of invisible substances made up of atoms in motion.

Material objects are of two kinds, atoms and compounds of atoms. The atoms themselves cannot be swamped by any force, for they are preserved indefinitely by their absolute solidity. Admittedly, it is hard to believe that anything can exist that is absolutely solid. The lightning stroke from the sky penetrates closed buildings, as do shouts and other noises. Iron glows molten in the fire, and hot rocks are cracked by untempered scorching. Hard gold is softened and melted by heat [and so on]. All these facts point to the conclusion that nothing is really solid. But sound reasoning and nature itself drives us to the opposite conclusion: that there exist certain bodies that are absolutely solid and indestructible, namely those atoms which according to our teaching are the seeds or prime units of things from which the whole universe is built up.

The point Lucretius is leading up to is that while the world-stuff, or atoms, are eternal and indestructible, they may take different forms (liquid, gaseous, and solid objects) that are ever-changing. So he carefully distinguishes between matter and the various forms it may take.

If the matter in things had not been everlasting, everything by now would have gone back to nothing, and the things we see would be the product of rebirth out of nothing. But since I have already shown that nothing can be created out of nothing nor any existing things be summoned back to nothing, the atoms must be made of imperishable stuff into which everything can be resolved in the end, so that there may be a stock of matter for building the world anew. The atoms, therefore, are absolutely solid and unalloyed. In no other way could they have survived throughout infinite time to keep the world in being.

Lucretius then speculates on the number of atoms in the Universe. He says that their number must be without limit and concludes that the Universe itself is infinite, "without end or measure." That idea was not to become acceptable in the leading universities of the world until the 1600s and 1700s. Lucretius cleverly provides us with an intellectual puzzle that the mentality of the old myth makers could neither understand nor appreciate:

Suppose for a moment that the whole of space were bounded and that someone made his way to its uttermost boundary and threw a flying dart. Do you suppose that the missile, hurled with might and main, would speed along the course on which it was aimed? Or do you think something would block the way and stop it? You must assume one alternative or the other. But neither of them leaves you a loophole. Both force you to admit that the universe continues without end. Whether there is some obstacle lying on the boundary line that prevents the dart from going farther on its course or whether it flies on beyond, it cannot in fact have started from the boundary. With this argument I will pursue you. Wherever you may place the ultimate limit of things, I will ask you: "Well then, what does happen to the dart?" The upshot is that the boundary cannot stand firm anywhere, and final escape from this conclusion is precluded by the limitless possibility of running away from it.

Lucretius next tells Memmius, in good materialist fashion, that the Universe and all in it have no purpose:

Certainly the atoms did not post themselves purposefully in due order by an act of intelligence, nor did they stipulate what movements each should perform. As they have been rushing everlastingly throughout all space in their myriads, undergoing myriad changes under the disturbing impact of collisions, they have experienced every variety of movement and conjunction till they have fallen into the particular pattern by which this world of ours is constituted. This world has persisted many a long year, having once been set going in the appropriate motions. From these everything else follows. The rivers replenish the thirsty sea with profuse streams of water. Incubated by the sun's heat, the earth renews its fruits, and the brood of animals that springs from it grows lustily. The gliding fires of ether sustain their life. None of these results would be possible if there were not an ample supply of matter to bounce up out of infinite space in replacement of all that is lost. Just as animals deprived of food waste away through loss of body, so everything must decay as soon as its supply of matter goes astray and is cut off.

At the time Lucretius lived, the Moon, Sun, and planets were the abodes of gods, and the stars were the departed souls of the dead. Here was a tightly closed little Universe with Earth located at the center and man the most "important" of all Earthly creatures. The new materialism preached by Lucretius opened an alternative window on the Universe and made it possible to ask new questions about what might lie out there in the dark, beyond the abodes of the gods. He tells us:

> *It is in the highest degree unlikely that this earth and sky is the only one to have been created.* . . . This follows from the fact that our world has been made by nature through the spontaneous and casual collision and the multifarious, accidental, random and purposeless congregation and coalescence of atoms whose suddenly formed combinations could serve on each occasion as the starting-point of substantial fabrics—earth and sea and sky and the races of living creatures. On every ground, therefore, you must admit that there exist elsewhere other congeries of matter similar to this one. . . . You have the same natural force to congregate them in any place precisely as they have been congregated here. You are bound therefore to acknowledge that in other regions there are other earths and various tribes of men and breeds of beasts.

In Lucretius we hear a voice of reason echoing the early Greek rationalists. The flickering torch of reason they lighted survived first the Roman conquest of Greece around 150 B.C. and then the fall of Rome some 650 years later. The barbarian hordes who swept down out of the north and destroyed Rome in effect turned history back a thousand years. The authoritarian voice of Christianity was made stronger when it became the only authorized religion of Rome around A.D. 380. As Judaism had been, the Christian church was intolerant of all points of view other than that of divine creation: God created the Universe and all life in it. Earth occupied the central position in the Solar System, and man occupied the central position among all of God's creatures. And that was that.

It was not until the 1500s and 1600s that astronomers upset the church-supported belief that Earth is the center of the Universe. They found that it is simply one of a number of planets circling a rather ordinary star, the Sun, and there was every reason to suppose that other Earth-like planets abounded out there in the dark and supported some kind of life, if not those forms of life familiar to us. Rational minds, once again, were searching for *natural* causes that operate the Universe. The friendly ghost of Lucretius had returned to haunt those who still made offerings to the gods: "Nature is free and uncontrolled by proud masters and runs the universe by herself without the aid of gods."

4

A NEW BEGINNING: THE UNIVERSE

Stars are the source of the energy by which all beings live. When the light of the last stars is extinguished life must end throughout the Universe.

—Robert Jastrow (1967)

Now suppose, as many people do, that people and beasts and plants and rocks did not arise suddenly in full bloom through an act of divine creation. Suppose instead that the Universe created itself or that it has always existed and goes on without beginning or end. Suppose also that life created itself by evolving out of nonliving matter and over hundreds of millions of years diversified into the forms known to us today. First, let's examine some of the ideas that have been proposed by astronomers, who are trying to find out what the Universe may have been like billions of years ago and what it may be like billions of years from now. Then we will be in a position to look at some of the ideas of biologists and chemists, who are trying to find out how life arose on Earth after the Sun and its family of planets had been formed.

ENTER COPERNICUS

By the mid-1500s the Roman, Greek, and Babylonian gods who for so long had directed the affairs of man from their abodes in the sky had become relics of the past. The pagan gods of old had gone down in defeat, yielding variously to the single god of Christianity, which had begun as a sect of Judiasm, whose one God was Yahweh, or to the one God of Islam. One of the Christian scholars of the 1500s was Nicolaus Copernicus, a Polish astronomer and canon of the Frauenberg cathedral. For years, from his small observatory in one of the towers of the cathedral, Copernicus had observed the nightly motion of the planets against the background of stars, as had the Greeks centuries earlier. The more he thought about those motions the more convinced he became that Earth was not the center of the Solar System, as had been taught for more than fifteen centuries.

Copernicus argued convincingly that the Sun, not Earth, occupied the central position in the Solar System and that Earth was simply one of the six planets then known. He further said, and in contradiction to the Bible, that Earth moves through space. First he explained that Earth rotates on its axis. It is that rotational motion, he said, that produces day and night and that causes the Sun, stars, and planets to appear to move across the sky from east to west. Then he reasoned that if it rotates why not suppose that it also revolves about the Sun?

These were the revolutionary ideas that were to help usher in the new astronomy some 70 years later. They also helped solidify astronomy as a science finally divorced from the super-

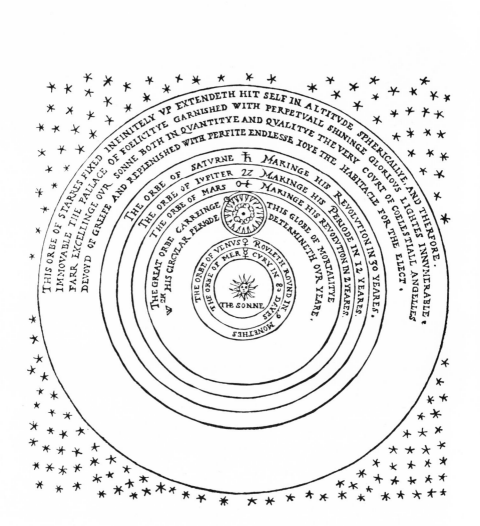

The following labels appear within the concentric circles of the diagram:

THIS ORBE OF STARRES FIXED INFINITELY VP EXTENDETH HIT SELF IN ALTITVDE SPHERICALLYE. AND THERFORE IMMOVABLE THE PALLACE OF FOELICITYE GARNISHED WITH PERPETVALL SHININGE GLORIOVS LIGHTES INNVMERABLE. FARR EXCELLINGE OVR SONNE BOTH IN QVANTITYE AND QVALITYE THE VERY COVRT OF COELESTIALL ANGELLES DEVOYD OF GREIFE AND REPLENISHED WITH PERFITE ENDLESSE IOYE THE HABITACLE FOR THE ELECT.

THE ORBE OF SATVRNE ♄ MAKINGE HIS REVOLVTION IN 30 YEARES.

THE ORBE OF IVPITER ♃ MAKINGE HIS PERIODE IN 12 YEARES.

THE ORBE OF MARS ♂ MAKINGE HIS REVOLVTION IN 2 YEARES.

THE GREAT ORBE CARREINGE THIS GLOBE OF MORTALITYE Wᵗʰ HIS CIRCVLAR PERIODE DETERMINETH OVR YEARE.

THE ORBE OF VENVS ♀ ROVLETH ROVND IN 9 MONETHES

THE ORBE OF MERCVRY ☿ ROVLETH ROVND IN 8 DAYES

THE SONNE

⚜ In the Universe imagined by Copernicus, the Sun occupied the central position. Other scholars later supposed that an infinite number of stars lay beyond the Sun's family of planets.

stitions of astrology and the authority of religious dogma. By moving Earth into a position of lesser importance, simply as the third planet from the Sun, Copernicus gave man reason to reevaluate his presumed position of importance in the Universe. Building on the ideas of Copernicus, other scholars reasoned that if Earth actually does rotate on its axis, then there is no longer any reason to suppose that the stars all are attached to a great crystal sphere that rotates on its axis and so carries the stars across the sky. In 1576 the Danish astronomer Tycho Brahe showed that the famous comet of that year was beyond the Moon and so had to have "passed through" a sphere or two. And two years earlier astronomers had been surprised to observe a star erupt violently as a "supernova." Such events surely were proof that the heavens could not be unchangeable.

If it was Earth's rotation that only made it appear that the stars moved, then there was no longer a need for the crystal sphere. First, the stars could be motionless in space; and second, they could lie at many different distances from Earth. Before very long, scholars were speaking of a Universe whose space could be infinite. If one puzzle had been solved, a new and far more complex one had taken its place. But then the history of astronomy has been a process largely of finding out what the Universe is not.

Today we envision space as a vast expanse dotted with billions upon billions of wheeling collections of stars called galaxies. Each galaxy, in turn, is made up of billions upon billions of stars, millions of which are thought to have planetary systems similar to our own Solar System. And lying among the stars are great clouds of gas and dust, the nebulae. Today we know that the stars are not motionless in space. As planets revolve about their central star, so do the stars revolve

❧ This German woodcut of the mid-1500s reflects the then growing idea that perhaps the outermost sphere of fixed stars was not the limit of the Universe after all.

✳ *Not until telescopes were invented could that hazy band we call the Milky Way be seen as a rich field of billions of stars. This view of star clouds is toward the center of the galaxy, in the Sagittarius region of the sky.* MOUNT WILSON AND PALOMAR OBSERVATORIES

about the central hub of their galaxy. And the galaxies themselves are in motion through space, a motion that suggests to astronomers at least two possible origins of the Universe.

❦❦❦

PLACING
THE SOLAR SYSTEM
IN TIME

❦❦❦

In our search for a creation scheme in keeping with all that we can observe about the Universe, the natural place to begin is that region of space we are most familiar with—the Solar System. But we must not lose sight of the fact that the Solar System is a complex collection of matter—nine planets accompanied by a total of thirty-three known satellites, hundreds of thousands of rock fragments called asteroids, most wheeling around in orbits between Mars and Jupiter, meteoroids and comets, and the Sun itself. Any theory that attempts to account for the origin of any one of these objects, but ignores any of the others, is not very helpful to us.

Were the Sun, planets, and other objects in the Solar System formed at just about the same time during one grand cosmic moment of creation, or is it possible that they came into being at different times? The evidence favors the first idea, that the Sun and planets originated at about the same time out of the same cosmic soup of raw materials.

Astronomers take a number of approaches to this problem. One is to examine the Sun. Based on a knowledge of the amount of hydrogen fuel the Sun has available to keep its nuclear furnace going and a knowledge of how rapidly the Sun is using up its fuel supply, astronomers tell us that the life span of a star like the Sun is about 10 billion years. But knowing the life span of the Sun does not tell us anything about its age. When astronomers talk about the age of a star or a planet, they mean the length of time the star or planet has been just about as we see it now—the length of time the Sun has been pouring out energy at its present rate, or the length of time Earth has had a solid crust and oceans.

Since we cannot reach up and tear a chunk out of the Sun in order to measure the age of its material, we are forced to examine those bits and pieces of the Solar System available to us—pieces of Earth rock, Moon rock, and cosmic stuff that rains down on Earth as meteorites. Because the "atomic clocks" used to measure the age of rocks, fossils, and other materials play such an important role in science, it is important to understand how these clocks work.

Since the late 1800s, scientists have known that the atoms of certain chemical elements said to be radioactive—such as uranium, potassium, and thorium—break down by giving up bits and pieces of themselves. In the process they turn into the atoms of other elements. For example, uranium turns into lead, as does thorium. Potassium turns into the element argon. It is easy to understand how these atomic clocks work if you imagine a large box with 12,800 black (uranium) marbles in it (Diagram 1). You want to find out how old the box of marbles is. Imagine that the black marbles age by turning gray. In one year, half of the black marbles turn gray (Diagram 2). At the end of the first year, there would be 6,400 black marbles left, plus 6,400 gray ones. At the end of the second year, half of the remaining 6,400 black marbles turn gray (Diagram 3). There would then be 3,200 black and 9,600 gray marbles. This process would go on and on until our clock ran down.

Passage of Time in Years	Number of Black Marbles	Number of Gray Marbles	Black-Gray Ratio
0	12,800	0	0
1	6,400	6,400	1 : 1
2	3,200	9,600	1 : 3
3	1,600	11,200	1 : 7
4	800	12,000	1 : 15
5	400	12,400	1 : 31
6	200	12,600	1 : 63
7	100	12,700	1 : 127
8	50	12,750	1 : 255
9	25	12,775	1 : 511

If you counted 800 black marbles and 12,000 gray ones, you would know that four years had gone by since the first black marble turned gray. But can you think of an easier way to tell how much time went by without counting *all* the marbles? Simply scoop a jarful of marbles—maybe 1,000—out of the box, count how many black and gray ones you have in the sample, and divide the number of gray ones by the number of black ones. This is the black-to-gray ratio (see right-hand column of table). In your sample of 1,000 marbles, there would be 61 black ones and 939 gray ones if the box were four years old, giving a ratio of 1:15.

That is how a radioactive clock works. Scientists measure the ratio between the number of unchanged atoms of a radioactive element and the number of new atoms that have been formed. The amount of time needed for half of the atoms of a radioactive element to change is called its *half-life*. Nothing seems to affect the half-life of any radioactive element—neither changes in temperature nor changes in pressure. Since the scientist knows the half-life of the radioactive element and since he can measure the ratio of the numbers of new and old atoms, he can then tell how long the clock has been running. Different radioactive elements have different half-lives. In the table are four radioactive elements that are used to date materials, three to date rocks, and one (carbon) to date material that was once alive.

THIS RADIOACTIVE ELEMENT	CHANGES INTO	AND HAS A HALF-LIFE OF
uranium–238	lead–206	4,510 million years
potassium–40	argon–40	1,350 million years
rubidium–40	strontium–87	6 million years
carbon–14	nitrogen–14	5,730 years

Usually, only very small amounts of a radioactive material are present in a rock being dated. This means that the slightest error in measurement may mean a large error in the ratio between the two elements. It would be like taking a sample of only 10 marbles, rather than 1,000. The point is that a sample of 1,000 will be more representative of the total of the blacks and grays among 12,800 marbles than would a sample of only 10 marbles. A slight error in measurement of a small radioactive sample may mean a difference of millions of years in the final absolute age figure. Just a 5 percent error in a 100-million-year-old rock might mean an error of 5 million years. This would be just a little less than 3 times the age of all humanity itself.

Scientists make two assumptions when they date materials by the radioactive decay method. First, in the potassium-argon series, for example, that no potassium or argon atoms have been added to the rock in question since it was formed and, second, that no argon atoms were present in the rock originally. Although many rocks and minerals are known to have contained some of the decay product (argon in our example),

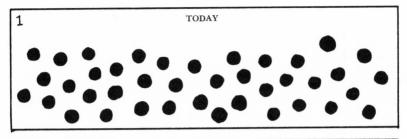

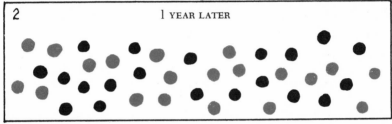

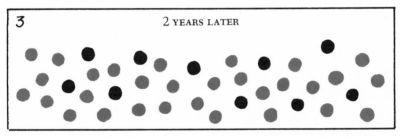

❦ *Measuring the half-life of a radioactive element (see text for explanation).* SCIENCE PHOTO/GRAPHICS, LTD.

geologists can determine how much of that decay product there was originally. They can then subtract that amount from the total amount of decay product measured and so end up with an accurate measurement of the amount produced by radioactive decay.

Geologists have used various radioactive elements to date rock samples from every corner of Earth and have come up with several ages. The oldest rocks from Earth's crust yet found are from Greenland and are 3.8 billion years old. Rocks from other regions—for example, near the Great Lakes and in certain parts of Europe—are 3.5 billion years old. It is very unlikely that Earth crustal rocks much older than the oldest samples presently known will turn up, but that does not mean that Earth was formed only 3.8 billion years ago. That age is for the crustal rock only, rock that went through its most recent geological change that long ago. While Earth has a recorded history going back at least 3.8 billion years, its history before that, or prehistory, is unknown to us by means of direct investigation.

The oldest Moon rocks that have yet been examined have a geologic history going back nearly a billion years earlier than the oldest Earth rocks. Meteorites now appear to be the senior citizens of the Solar System. Radioactive dating of many stony and iron meteorites shows an average age of about 4.7 billion years. If we accept that as an approximate age of the Solar System, then Earth went through about 1 billion years of geological and chemical evolution before a crust of solid rock developed. So all the evidence points to an age somewhere around 5 billion years for the formation of the Sun, planets, and other objects making up the Solar System. That is a far cry from an age of 6,000 years assigned by Archbishop Ussher and upheld to this day by certain creationists.

※※※

FORMING
THE SOLAR SYSTEM
IN SPACE

※※※

The ancient Greeks were not experimenters; they were magnificent theorists. It was not until the time of the Italian scientist Galileo in the 1600s, and then later in the 1700s, that scientists began emphasizing the importance of experimenting —conducting a test to find out what will happen, not to prove that something is true. During this period experiments with gases were opening the way for the discovery of the chemical elements oxygen, hydrogen, chlorine, and others. Experiments in physics were framing the laws that explain the motion of falling objects, whether those objects were as small as atoms or as large as planets and stars.

Around the mid-1700s ideas suggesting how the Sun and planets were formed began to appear. Of the several hypotheses, all can be grouped into two main classes—catastrophic and nebular. Those of the catastrophic school imagine a ready-made Sun that was disturbed by a passing star or other large object that strayed close to the Sun. During the flyby, gravitational attraction caused a great cloud of material to be torn out of both objects and set free around the Sun. The planets and all other objects of the Solar System presumably were formed out of this cast-off material. Such an encounter would give rise to *two* planetary systems, one for each star.

The nebular hypothesis has as its starting point a large, cold cloud of gas and dust out of which the Sun and its planets alike were formed. In 1755 the German philosopher Immanuel Kant published a book setting forth a nebular hypothesis. Kant was concerned with the mechanical origin of the Solar System according to the law of gravitation developed by Isaac Newton nearly a century earlier. During the seventeenth and eighteenth centuries the thinking of many scientists was strongly influenced by the Christian church, and they avoided making public statements that in any way contradicted what the church held to be true. Kant, for example, began his book almost defensively by saying that it should not be considered irreverent to inquire into the origin of the Universe by considering the laws of nature. After all, he argued, those very laws were given to man by God, along with a brain to investigate them.

Kant's starting point was a Universe throughout which gas was distributed more or less uniformly. However, here and there were volumes of space with somewhat higher than average concentrations of gas. Such regions, he said, would be collecting grounds for a massive buildup of matter. Didn't Newton's law of gravitation say that the more massive an object, the greater the force with which it attracts other objects? The gravitational force of a nebula would cause it to draw more and more material into itself toward the region of greatest concentration of mass. As it did, the great cloud would begin to spin around and flatten out as a disk. Kant imagined a great ball-shaped concentration of gas near the center of the cloud and a thinner distribution out toward the edge. In the core region of the cloud, he said, the gases began to pack themselves tightly and soon formed a dense central bulge that eventually became the Sun. Meanwhile, gas forming the disk material developed patches of greater concentration than the surrounding gases. These smaller gas clouds within the disk gases would also begin to rotate and form smaller planet-sized masses.

The general plan of Kant's nebular hypothesis is the one astronomers use today, although they do not go along with most of Kant's detailed explanations of the forces causing the cloud to behave as he described it. Also, they have added many chemical and physical refinements that could not possibly have been included by Kant. At the time Kant proposed his nebular hypothesis, it was not possible to disprove it.

A relatively recent theory accounting for the formation of the Solar System is one developed by the German astronomer Carl von Weizsäcker, Gerard Kuiper, and others. This theory

❊ *There is strong evidence that stars are formed out of dense concentrations of gas and stellar dust called "globules." Several dark globules can be seen in this nebula photographed in the constellation of Monoceros (NGC 2237).* MOUNT WILSON AND PALOMAR OBSERVATORIES

takes us back to Kant's gas and dust cloud. About 5 billion years ago the cloud extended about 10 billion miles in diameter. Under gravitational attraction the cloud gradually closed in on itself, spinning and flattening until it eventually became a huge rotating disk like the one pictured by Kant. About 95 percent or more of the cloud's gas and dust formed a sphere at the center of the disk. It was this densely packed globe of matter that eventually began to glow a dull red as it heated up and became a new star.

A great wheel of leftover material extended outward from the Sun's equator to a distance of about three billion miles—about the present distance from the sun of the planet Neptune. Like a phonograph record, the gas and dust making up the disk spun around the rotating solar hub. Within the disk many whirlpools formed, broke up, and formed again, but some of the larger and denser ones did not break up. They held together and swept up large amounts of surrounding gas and dust, growing more massive in the process. At least eight such whorls formed, each taking the shape of a sphere and eventually becoming one of the planets known to us today.

Kuiper estimates that the formation of such solar disks massive enough to produce planetary systems is rather common, there being one planetary system for every 100 to 1,000 stars. If correct, that would mean that in our home galaxy alone, the Milky Way, or simply the Galaxy, there are some 1 billion or more planetary systems.

At first, the young Sun was a cool globe of gas that gradually drew large amounts of nearby disk material into itself. However, farther out in the disk, at about the present distance of Jupiter, where the Sun's gravitational attraction was weaker because of the greater distance, large amounts of disk material remained. This would account for the fact that Mercury, Venus, Earth, and Mars are relatively small planets compared with the more distant and massive Jupiter, Saturn, Uranus, and Neptune.

Internal gravitation of the young Sun caused it to collapse in on itself, in the process packing with tremendous force its material in the core region. As the material became more and more tightly packed, the Sun continued to heat up and became increasingly brighter. During these early years in the formation of the Solar System, then, astronomers picture the young Sun as a relatively cool red object producing energy in a way quite different from the way it does now. Surrounding the new Sun was a dense fog of gas and dust through which the newly forming planets moved. Space throughout the Solar System at this time must have been opaque. As this material was continually being swept up by the young planets, hydrogen atoms in the fog probably were combining with carbon atoms and producing the gas methane (CH_4). Hydrogen also would be combining with nitrogen atoms and producing ammonia (NH_3), and with oxygen atoms to produce water vapor (H_2O).

Evidence for such a process of the building up of heavier groupings of atoms comes not only from the laboratory, but from our studies of the giant planets Jupiter and Saturn. Because of their large mass, gravity on those planets is much stronger than on Earth. This means that while Earth could not hold on to its primitive atmosphere, Jupiter and Saturn kept much of theirs. To this day the atmospheres of those giant planets probably are the same as when the planets were formed. They are known to consist of methane, ammonia, water vapor, hydrogen, and helium. But by far the most of their matter is hydrogen and helium.

After about 100 million years, the Sun became much hotter and began to shine as we see it today. When it did, the energy

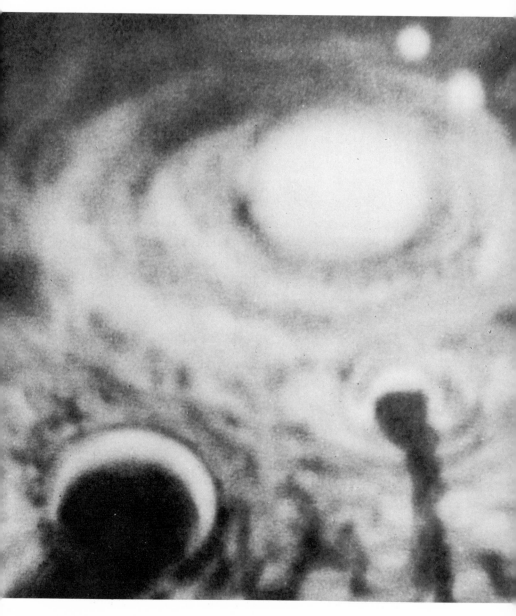

※ *Artist's version of the densely "foggy" Solar System as the Sun (center) and its planets were being formed some five billion years ago.* COURTESY: CATHIE POLGREEN

it gave off acted as a wind and began to clear the foggy gas, eventually pushing the material out of the Solar System. We can see the effects of such a "solar wind," as it is called, when we watch a comet circle the Sun, the solar wind keeping the tail of the comet always pointed away from the Sun. With the expulsion of this cosmic fog, space between the planets eventually became transparent as it is today.

Just as the young Sun had a disk of gas and dust spinning around it, so did each of the newly formed planets. Within these planetary disks whorls developed and became satellites of the planets. Just as the planets are spread out in a line with the Sun's equator—the plane of the original solar disk—most of the satellites in the Solar System also lie near a plane formed by each planet's equator.

Although no one can say for certain that the Sun and its family of planets were formed just that way, all the evidence points to some such process. In any case, it seems virtually certain that planets are by-products of star formation and that the stars themselves originate out of the nebulae, those vast collections of gas and dust that occur in great abundance throughout the Galaxy.

✻✻✻

STARS:
THE ELEMENT FACTORIES

✻✻✻

The ancient Greeks spoke of the basic stuff of the Universe as the four root "elements"—earth, air, fire, and water. The elements that chemists speak of today are much simpler substances—hydrogen, oxygen, gold, lead, and uranium, for example. Each element has only one kind of atom. Hydrogen, the simplest element of all, contains a central core, or nucleus, of one particle called a proton, around which a much smaller particle, an electron, moves. The second simplest element is helium, consisting of four particles in its central core (two protons plus two other particles called neutrons) with two orbiting electrons. Other elements have much more complex atoms: an atom of gold, for instance, has 197 particles in its core and 79 electrons.

Of the 106 known elements that make up planet Earth, about 70 of them have been detected in the surface gases of the Sun. So when we ask where the elements composing Earth came from, we look to the Sun as the most reasonable source since the original disk material is no longer available. Of all the elements, the two simplest ones, hydrogen and helium, make up nearly all of the Sun; and of those two, there is much more hydrogen than helium. So we can picture the original Solar System cloud of gas and dust as an "alphabet soup" of gaseous elements mixed up with dust particles, simple aggregates of certain kinds of atoms. Eight out of every 10 atoms of that original nebula were hydrogen, and most of the rest were helium, with perhaps 1 in 1,000 being atoms of heavier elements such as oxygen, carbon, and iron. At least, that is the picture suggested by the present composition of the Sun.

If the material making up planet Earth and everything on it came from the original cloud of matter that became the Sun, then we must ask where the material making up that cloud came from. And that, of course, is the same as asking where all of the nebulae in the Galaxy came from. The stars themselves are the element factories of the Universe. In the course of its lifetime a newly formed star heats up until its core temperature reaches many millions of degrees; a star like the Sun, for example, has a core temperature of about 15 million degrees. At these high temperatures, the single protons that are the nuclei

❀ *The Great Nebula in Orion (NGC 1976). There is enough gas and dust in this nebula to form about 3,000 stars, each as massive as the Sun.* HALE OBSERVATORIES

✳ *The "Crab" Nebula (NGC 1952) in the constellation of Taurus is the remains of a supernova star that exploded in the year* A.D. *1054. To date, astronomers know of only three supernovae in our galaxy.*

MOUNT WILSON AND PALOMAR OBSERVATORIES

of hydrogen atoms smash into each other with great force and fuse. This process of fusion builds up the nuclei of helium atoms. And at still higher temperatures the helium nuclei fuse and form the nuclei of carbon. In this way some 25 elements, but none heavier than iron, are manufactured in the cores of stars.

Eventually, however, there must come a day when a star uses up the last of its hydrogen supply. At such a time a star may change its life style in a number of ways. One way is to blow itself to bits as a *supernova.* Such supernova explosions seem to be very rare events, however. Only three have been recorded: the Guest Star of the year 1054, shown here, another that exploded in 1572 (Tycho's Nova), and another in 1604 (Kepler's Nova). But radio telescopes provide evidence of a dozen or so more. Perhaps there are as few as one a century in the Galaxy. During a supernova explosion clouds of matter are returned to space, clouds made up of complex atoms, which over the millions of years of the star's life had been built up out of the original raw material of the Universe—hydrogen. The Sun and other so-called second generation stars are made up of just such secondhand material, in the case of our Sun material that was cast off into space by aging stars more than five billion years ago. Because only exceptionally massive stars become supernovae, these stars are very rare. Most stars that we can observe are not much more than 10 times more massive or less massive than the Sun. It now seems that for a star to become a supernova it must be from about 50 to 100 times more massive than the Sun.

At the present time the great majority of matter in the Galaxy does not exist as nebulae out of which stars are forming. Although many new stars are in the process of forming out of nebulae at the present time, only 5 percent or so of the total matter making up the entire Galaxy exists as gas and dust between the stars. As more and more of this 5 percent of free matter is swept up in new star formation and becomes locked up as star matter, fewer and fewer stars can be formed.

Eventually, it would appear, there will come a time when no more new stars can be formed in the Galaxy, because there simply will not be enough loose matter around. When that day arrives, we will be a member of a dying galaxy. The great majority of stars do not blow themselves to bits and so provide the raw materials for new star formation. Instead, they die quietly by collapsing and cooling off until they are relatively small objects shining very dimly and one day going out. Eventually, then, our Galaxy, like all others, is destined to fade as the stars flicker out one by one. In time the Galaxy will be a dark place of some 150 billion black dwarf stars. Will that distant day, we may ask, be the end of the world, the end of the Universe? The end of life on Earth, certainly, but perhaps not the end of life, or of the Universe.

❧❧❧

AN AGE FOR THE UNIVERSE

❧❧❧

Although astronomers disagree over many fine points of the theories about what happens inside stars and how stars age, they are in general agreement about several larger ideas: (1) that stars are born out of the nebulae, shine for tens of millions or for billions of years, and then die; (2) that galaxies, too, were born out of the supernebulae, then after billions of years fade to dimness as their stars go out; (3) that the Universe of galaxies appears to be expanding, meaning that we see galaxies rushing away from us in all direction; (4) that all of the galaxies we can see are distributed fairly evenly through space.

There are as many in any one direction of the sky as there are in any other direction.

What all of this means is another matter. In a way, we are in a fix similar to the one the ancient Greek astronomers were in, only ours is on a much larger scale. The Greeks could follow the paths traced by the planets across the "surface" of the sky, but they had difficulty envisioning those paths in three-dimensional space. Today we can detect certain motions of the galaxies—a general rushing away from us and from each other—but we cannot envision a shape or limit to the space occupied by those galaxies.

澡

A STEADY-STATE UNIVERSE

澡

What if the galaxies, like the stars, are not all the same age? Then some of the galaxies we now see out there are old, some young, and others middle-aged. While some are dying and fading out of sight, others are being born out of supernebulae. According to the steady-state theory, there is always enough hydrogen gas between the galaxies to form new galaxies. As ten, twenty, or a thousand galaxies fade from view, ten, twenty, or a thousand new ones are being formed and replenishing the Universe. In this way there is a more or less constant number of galaxies all the time and the Universe always remains pretty much the way we see it now. But what happens to the old "dead" galaxies?

To date no one has detected one. Another bothersome question about the steady-state theory of the Universe is where does the infinite supply of hydrogen for new galaxy formation come from? To date, there is no evidence for its existence. According to the founders of this theory—Thomas Gold, Fred Hoyle, and Herman Bondi—the creation of one hydrogen atom per year in a volume of space equal to that of the Empire State Building is enough to keep the Universe in a steady state. As the galaxies continue to rush away from each other and leave gaps of increasing size, new galaxies come into being and fill the gaps, say the steady-state theorists. So we must picture a Universe in which the density of matter remains constant while the volume increases. But where do the new hydrogen atoms required to keep density constant come from?

According to Gold, they create themselves out of nothing. Many astronomers find it as difficult to accept that idea as accepting the creation myths that have monsters slaying each other and constructing the Universe piece by piece out of severed limbs. The steady-state theory violates a fundamental law of physics that has been around for a long time, the principle of the conservation of mass and energy. That law says that matter can be neither created nor destroyed. According to the astronomer Robert Jastrow, "it seems difficult to accept a theory that ignores such a firmly established fact of terrestrial experience."

※※※

A BIG-BANG UNIVERSE

※※※

As we look around us in space we see the galaxies in all directions rushing away from us. The more distant ones appear to be rushing away the fastest, the nearer ones more slowly. Suppose, for a moment, that we could reverse time and make it run backward. The galaxies suddenly stop in their tracks, and then begin backing up, each one moving in toward us at exactly its rushing-away speed. If we imagine the galaxies to continue moving this way, what is bound to happen? They would retrace their paths and eventually come together in one region of space.

If we suppose that all of the galaxies actually were together in one region of space at some distant time in the past, when was it? When astronomers measure the speeds and distances of a great many of the galaxies and clusters of galaxies, they find that nearly every one began its outward journey about 10 billion years ago, twice the age of the Solar System. If the galaxy known a M60 set out from our region of space 10 billion years ago and if it has been traveling around 680 miles per second ever since, it would now be nearly 30 million light-years away. (A light-year is the distance traveled by light in one year at the rate of 186,000 miles per second, or about 6 trillion miles.) And that is the distance from us at which we find it now. And so with other individual galaxies and clusters of galaxies, as shown in the table.

Galaxy	Speed (miles/ second)	Distance (millions of light-years)	Cluster of Galaxies	Speed (miles/ second)	Distance (millions of light-years)
M64	93	7	Perseus	3,370	179
M82	186	13	Pegasus II	7,900	490
M63	280	18	Corona		
M65	500	25	Borealis	13,500	820
M96	590	29	Ursa		
M60	680	38	Major 2	25,000	1,560
			Hydra	37,500	1,960
			3C 295	85,600	5,700
			(a quasar)		
			Other quasars	near speed of light	10,000 to 15,000

If the galaxies, presently seen to be expanding into space, were in fact together in one small region of space some 10 to

15 billion years ago, then does that time mark the beginning of the Universe? According to the big-bang theory, which was developed by the Belgian astronomer-priest Father Lemaître and the physicist George Gamow, this was the state of cosmic affairs some 10 to 15 billion years ago. And before that there were no galaxies, just a great superdense cloud of gas, a cosmic egg of sorts. Something caused the cloud to expand violently and rush outward in all directions. The gas broke up into individual clouds that became the galaxies. Within each galaxy-cloud still smaller clouds gave birth to star clusters and to individual stars. And as some of the individual stars formed, "leftover" gas and dust packed itself into planets. However, some of the gas and dust never formed stars and remains as free matter thinly spread out in space among the stars.

In our brief lifetime, a mere tick of the cosmic clock, we see ourselves as part of a Universe that is expanding. But what happens next? Some astronomers say that the galaxies may keep on rushing outward in all directions without end. In a long cosmic sigh the Universe may be gradually dispersing or spreading ever outward. Others have said that the expansion eventually may slow down and stop. The galaxies will then begin to move back toward the region where they were formed. They will all come together and be pressed into a mammoth sphere which will explode, and the process will start all over again.

Like the steady-state theory, this version of the big-bang theory—the universal oscillation theory—has us living in a Universe without beginning or end. We are told that about 10 billion years ago a big bang began a new cycle. While the galaxies are now speeding outward because of the momentum generated by this last big bang, gravitation exerts a braking action on the galaxies. Eventually, they will be stopped in their tracks and begin falling back in toward the center of the Universe again until they smash together. Another big bang will then begin the cycle anew, and it will go on and on forever. One estimate says that one complete cycle takes about 80 billion years, 40 for expansion and another 40 for contraction. So we would now be about a quarter of the way along an expansion phase.

At this stage of our knowledge, the evidence tends to favor the big-bang theory. But there is evidence against a big-bang theory that has the Universe pulsating in cycles of death and rebirth. In their exploration of the Universe, the astronomer and the physicist today are at two great frontiers of science. Having pulled that vague atom of Democritus to bits and pieces, physicists are now trying to discover a meaningful pattern in its bewildering variety of parts. But the more they look, the more bits and pieces they find and the more confusing the picture seems to become. It would seem that they are learning more and more about less and less. At the opposite end of the scale, astronomers also are trying to fit bits and pieces together to find a pattern, but the more they find, the more confusing the picture seems to become for them also. In this case it would seem that they are learning less and less about more and more. However, both groups are exploring worlds that could not be imagined by the ancient Babylonians and Greeks or even as recently as the early 1900s.

One of the most profound questions man has ever asked still remains unanswered: How did the Universe begin (if it ever had a beginning), and how will it end (if it ever does end)? Like the old patent medicines that promised to cure one and all of our ailments, the myths of old had built-in answers to any question that could be asked. Nothing was too fantastic for them to explain. Science does not make such extravagant claims. In fact, it does not provide any assurance whatever that it will come up with the answers we seek. Nevertheless, if there is a better way of investigating the physical nature of the Universe than that of scientific inquiry, it has yet to be invented.

5

A NEW BEGINNING: LIFE

It is often said that all the conditions for the first production of a living organism are now present, which could ever have been present. But if (and oh what a big if) we could conceive in some warm little pond, with all sorts of ammonia and phosphoric acid salts, light, heat, electricity, etc., present, that a protein compound was chemically formed ready to undergo still more complex changes, at the present day such matter would be instantly devoured, or absorbed, which would not have been the case before living creatures were formed.

—Charles Darwin (1859)

Only during the last few decades have chemists and biologists been designing experiments in an attempt to find out how living things might have arisen out of what at first seems a very unlikely source—nonliving matter. But then, "There is no *fundamental* difference between a living organism and lifeless matter," the Russian biochemist A. I. Oparin tells us. The idea of life arising from nonliving matter is not new. The ancient Babylonians, Egyptians, and Greeks, among others, all had myths relating how supernatural forces created life out of nonliving materials.

SPONTANEOUS GENERATION

To this day you can still find superstitious people who believe that if they put a horse's hair or a woman's hair into a container of water the hair will turn into a snake if left long enough. In the 1600s the well-known scientist J. B. van Helmont gave a recipe for producing mice:

> If a dirty undergarment is squeezed into the mouth of a vessel containing wheat, within a few days (say 21) a ferment drained from the garments and transformed by the smell of the grain, encrusts the wheat itself with its own skin and turns it into mice. . . . And, what is more remarkable, the mice from corn and undergarments are neither weanlings or sucklings nor premature but they jump out fully formed.

Furthermore, van Helmont claimed to have carried out the experiment himself. The mice that are produced, he said, immediately mate and produce more mice. Still earlier, Aristotle taught that fleas and mosquitoes are generated spontaneously out of decaying matter and that fireflies arise out of morning dew. The Roman poet Vergil described a swarm of bees arising out of the carcass of a cow. Many others believed that mice, flies, and other lower animals could arise fully formed out of dust, mud, and particularly out of decaying meat and the dead flesh of fish. Lucretius wrote:

And even now we see full many a breed
Of living creatures rise out of the earth
Begot by rains and by the genial warmth
The Sun doth shed.

Nearly always such beliefs in a process of *spontaneous generation* have at least some basis in "fact." To put it more accurately, nearly always such beliefs are the result of drawing incorrect conclusions from observation. For example, the ancient Egyptians were convinced that mice were generated spontaneously from mud. This was an incorrect conclusion based on the correct observation that sudden plagues of mice occurred each year after the Nile flooded its banks. Silt carried down by the flood waters supposedly was the matter out of which the mice were created.

Through the scholastic desert years of the Dark Ages people continued to believe in spontaneous generation. It wasn't until the mid-1600s that physicians began to test the idea and challenge it. One such man was an Italian named Francesco Redi. He performed experiments showing that maggots, which are the larval stage of flies, are not generated spontaneously by rotting meat and the dead flesh of fish. He got the idea for his experiments from something he had observed.

Redi had put three dead snakes in a box and from time to time examined them as they decayed. Soon he noticed that maggots were crawling over the decaying meat and eating it. After several days there was nothing left of the snakes except their bones. Nineteen days after he had put the dead snakes in the box, many of the maggots became inactive and formed themselves into hard balls, what we now know to be the pupal stage in the life cycle of a fly. At the time, however, the idea of life cycles of insects was very poorly understood, although Redi was aware that caterpillars similarly go through a pupal stage

❀ *This old woodcut from a Turkish history of India shows a tree that grows human fruit. It wasn't until the 1600s that scientists began to propound the notion that living things normally can give rise only to offspring of their own kind (species).*

when they spin a cocoon. The idea of a living organism changing its form seemed difficult to accept.

Redi next placed some of the maggot pupae into a jar to find out what would happen to them. About a week later each pupa broke open, and out came an adult fly. Could it be, Redi asked himself, that the maggots are not created out of dead meat but hatch from tiny eggs laid on the meat by adult flies? It was a hypothesis, an educated guess, and he lost no time in testing it by designing an experiment.

He put a dead snake in one jar, a dead eel in another, dead flesh from a calf in a third, and some fish flesh in a fourth. Then he did exactly the same with four other identical jars. While he left the first set of jars open to the air, he closed off the tops of the second set by capping them tightly. As he examined both sets each day he noticed that flies were entering and leaving the open jars, and within a few days he also noticed that maggots were crawling over the meat in all four of the open jars. There wasn't a single maggot on any of the meat in the four closed jars.

Some people would stop there, confident that they had enough evidence. But Redi was cautious. Possibly maggots did not appear in the closed jars because *air*, not flies, had been kept out. He repeated the experiment as before. But this time instead of sealing one set of jars tightly, he tied off their tops with a very fine netting. This would permit air to flow in but would keep out flies. Flies were attracted to the jars by the odor but were unable to get in. When maggots did not develop on the meat, Redi concluded that flies are not generated spontaneously but are produced by other flies. Other experimenters performed similar investigations involving other kinds of animals. When they all got the same results it seemed certain that living things were produced only by other living things. That life arises only from living things, a concept known as *biogenesis*, and not from nonliving matter, became one of the foundation stones of biology.

But old ideas die hard, and biogenesis was not to catch on instantly. During Redi's time the microscope came into common use, and it wasn't long before a whole new world of microscopic organisms was commanding the attention of biologists. A major question was, "How do *these* tiny organisms originate?" One of the first users of a microscope was the Dutch experimenter Anton van Leeuwenhoek, who in the late 1600s began recording his fascination over the inhabitants of this new and mysterious world of living things that he called *animalcules*:

> In the year 1675 I discover'd living creatures in rain water, which had stood but a few days in a new earthen pot. . . . This invited me to view this water with great attention, especially those little animals appearing to me ten thousand times less than . . . water-fleas, which may be perceived in the water with the naked eye. . . . [Having mixed pepper in water and letting it remain about three weeks], I twice added some snowwater, the other water being in great part exhaled; I looked upon it the 24 of April, 1676, and discerned in it, to my great wonder, an incredible number of little animals of diverse kinds; and among the rest, some that were 3 or 4 times as long as broad; but their whole thickness did, in my estimation, not much exceed that of the hair of a louse. They had a very pretty motion, often tumbling about and sideways; and when I let the water run off from them, they turned as round as a top, and at first their body changed into an oval, and afterwards, when the circular motion ceased, they returned to their former length.

Where did the hundreds of different kinds of these tiny creatures come from? Were they subject to the law of biogenesis, or, since they were so simple, could they be generated from nonliving material? The whole argument over spontaneous generation opened up again, since it was impossible to observe any eggs or seeds from which these elusive microscopic organisms developed. If a few strands of hay were placed in pure water, a few days later the water was swarming with the creatures.

Around 1700 Louis Jablot designed an experiment similar to those of Redi. He put some hay into a container of water and then boiled it to kill all living matter that it might contain. Then he poured half the boiled material into a second container and tightly sealed it. After a few days he examined the contents of both containers. While he couldn't find a single living thing in the material from the sealed container, the material from the container that had been left open swarmed with life. He concluded that any material that has been sterilized cannot possibly generate life. The living organisms in the container that had been left open, he said, had drifted in from the air.

The problem of spontaneous generation was settled once and for all by the French scientist Louis Pasteur in the 1800s. This was after the French Academy had offered a prize to anyone able to settle the spontaneous generation argument. Pasteur experimented with many different kinds of microscopic organisms and showed two things to be true: (1) that a long enough boiling time would kill all such organisms in milk, wine, water, meat broth, and other substances, and (2) that on exposure to the air, all such substances become infected with bacteria. Pasteur, in a wonderfully simple experiment, proved beyond a doubt that "germs" did not arise spontaneously in such substances. There were still some die-hard believers in spontaneous generation who said that there was a special life-giving substance contained in the air, so naturally if you kept air from a purified substance life could not possibly be generated by that substance. Pasteur's experiment dealt the final blow to this notion.

He made a glass flask with a long neck that narrowed to an opening about the size of a pinhole. Milk, beef broth, or any other purified substance put in these swan-neck flasks remained purified even though air could enter the flask through the fine opening. What happened was that when bacteria in the air drifted in through the tiny opening they hit the side of the glass tubing and stuck there. He could show that this was so simply by tilting the flask until some of the liquid ran down and sloshed around near the end and was then allowed to run back into the main part of the flask. The bacteria washed back with it soon multiplied and formed a thriving culture.

In still another experiment Pasteur boiled broth in an ordinary flask and then plugged the end with a piece of sterile cotton. Even though air was entering the flask through the cotton, living organisms did not appear in the broth. When he removed the cotton, washed it, and then examined the wash water, he found it teeming with bacteria that had been filtered out during the experiment. In a now-famous speech about his experiments, Pasteur said:

> I could point to [a] liquid and say to you, I have taken my drop of water from the immensity of creation, and I have taken it full of the elements appropriated to the development of inferior beings. And I wait, I watch, I question it, begging it to recommence for me the beautiful spectacle of the first creation. But it was dumb . . . it is dumb because I have kept it from air, from life, for life is a germ and a germ is life. *Never will the doctrine of spontaneous generation recover from the mortal blow of this simple experiment.*

Pasteur's experiments represent one of the most important triumphs of reason over superstition.

❊❊❊

FOSSILS:
LINKS WITH THE PAST

❊❊❊

At the time Pasteur was carrying out his experiments that were to crush the superstition of spontaneous generation, other scientists were chipping away at myths that had for so long masked the nature of fossils, our links with the past.

Among the ancient Greek scholars, Xenophanes, who lived in
the fifth century b.c., had found fossils of fish far inland and
correctly identified them for what they were. He also said that
in the dim past parts of the land had been covered by the sea
and that is why marine fossils were found high up in the mountains. During the Dark Ages, however, most people preferred
to believe that fossils were the work of the Devil when he tried
unsuccessfully to create animals.

Leonardo da Vinci was among the first to take up the serious
study of fossils again around 1600. His keen deductions were
an echo of Xenophanes. He said that the fossils of marine animals he had observed in northern Italy had once been living
organisms that had died during a period when the sea covered
that part of Italy. Mud next covered them in layers, and the
mud layers eventually turned into rock. In time the mass was
uplifted as land. But again, old ideas die hard. It was clearly
stated in the first chapter of Genesis that the land and the sea
were divided on the third day of creation: "Let the waters
under heaven be gathered together unto one place, and let
the dry land appear: and it was so."

Since God did not create animals until the fifth and sixth
days of creation, it seemed difficult to understand how marine
animals could have appeared on the land since they were
created after the land had been formed. There was, of course,
a way out of this problem: all marine fossils found on land
had been washed there during the Noachian flood and were,
therefore, approximately 6,000 years old.

As early as the 1600s, scientists knew that older layers of
rock are always covered by younger layers. Around 1800, the
English surveyor and engineer William Smith noticed that
different rock layers had different kinds of fossils. Any single
rock layer, however, usually contained the same kinds of fossils.

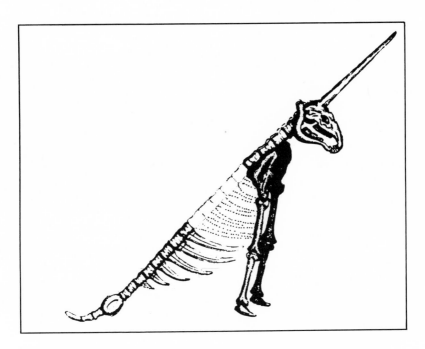

❦ *When fossils first came under serious study in the 1700s, a number of fanciful reconstructions appeared as a result of piecing together a "whole" animal from scattered individual bones. A German physicist named Otto von Guericke in 1749 assembled isolated fossil bones into a complete skeleton of the mythical unicorn.*

After a while Smith became so skillful that he could tell from which layer of rock a given fossil had been collected.

At about the same time, two French geologists were studying and mapping the extent of the fossil-bearing strata that surround Paris. Both George Cuvier and Alexandre Brongniart also discovered that certain fossils were found only in certain rock layers. As the two arranged their collections of fossils in the same order as the rocks from which they came, they discovered something else. They learned that the fossils changed in an orderly way from layer to layer. Cuvier and Brongniart compared the fossil forms with the more modern forms of life. It soon became evident that the fossils from the higher, and therefore younger, rock layers were more similar to modern forms of life than those fossils from older rock layers lower down.

While some scientists had begun to suspect that animals and plants alike had evolved, or changed from one form into others over the ages, Cuvier could not accept this idea. He firmly believed that animal and plant species were "immutable," or unchangeable. Once created by God, each species remained forever the same, he said. When asked to explain why an older layer of rock contained fossils of plants and animals that never were found in younger layers near the top, Cuvier said that a flood or some other world catastrophe struck and killed all living things in a certain region. Then after the catastrophe new animals and plants from other parts of the world migrated to the stricken region and repopulated it with new and different kinds of living things. When other catastrophes occurred, the same process of repopulation followed, and this accounted for each rock layer having its own distinctive kinds of fossils. Or so it seemed. Cuvier's explanation failed entirely to account for the fact that the fossils from the younger rock layers were more similar to modern forms of life than those fossils from deeper layers (see the Geologic Time Chart). Nevertheless, the idea of the periodic wholesale destruction of populations of animals and plants appealed to many, as it does to this day, and became known as *catastrophism*.

Shown on the following pages is the geological time scale for the history of Earth worked out by scientists who study rocks and fossils. While the Period is the most important division in this time scale, the different periods are grouped under the larger division called the Era. Most of the names given to the periods are place names for localities where rocks of that age were first studied and described. On the other hand, Tertiary (meaning "third") and Quaternary (meaning "fourth") are names retained from an earlier four-fold division of the rocks.

As earth scientists' knowledge about the rocks and their fossils grows year by year, from time to time it is necessary to change our ideas about the times when certain geologic events took place. For example, in 1961 geologists established that the Silurian Period began 425 million years ago and ended 405 million years ago. In the light of new evidence, these figures were changed recently to a beginning date of 430 million years and a closing date of 395 million years. As a result of this change, the time span of the Silurian Period was nearly doubled. Aso in 1961 the Pleistocene Epoch had a beginning date of one million years ago. But more recently this figure was revised to 2.0 million years ago, again doubling the length of the period. As instruments and techniques used to measure the age of minerals become more accurate, the geologic calendar will continue to be revised and made more precise.

Cuvier could not accept the idea of life evolving through geologic time; neither could many other scientists of the 1800s whose religious faith overpowered their ability to reason objectively to interpret the fossil record. A large number of them went further than Cuvier had by saying that after each catastrophe that wiped out entire species from the fossil record, God created new species to replace those He had destroyed during the catastrophe. On the one hand, then, were the creationists, who looked to supernatural forces for an explanation of the origin of the Universe, the origin of life, and all that could be read in the fossil record. And on the other was a growing number of scientists who felt that the fossil record could be accurately read only if natural causes were searched out to account for the great pageant of life extending back in time for hundreds of millions of years.

THE AGES OF EARTH ✳✳ A Geological Time Chart

ERA	PERIOD	THE LAND	THE SEA	BIOLOGICAL EVENTS
CENOZOIC *(from the Greek words* kainos, *meaning "recent" and* zoe, *meaning "life")*	QUATERNARY (meaning "fourth") Present to 2.0 million years ago	The Cascadian Disturbance deformed the Coast Ranges of the west coast of North America and caused widespread volcanic activity. This disturbance probably is still going on today.	Continental glaciers developed on the continents of North Antarctica, while valley glaciers formed in the high mountain regions. There were four glacial and three interglacial ages. The heights of the sea varied with the formation and melting of ice.	Modern horses appeared at the beginning of this period. Of the several manlike animals that developed, only one species (*Homo sapiens*) survived and occurs in great numbers today. Glaciation caused the extinction of great mammals and many trees.
	TERTIARY (meaning "third") 2.0 million to 65 million years ago	There was widespread volcanic activity in the western United States. Mounts Shasta and Rainier were formed, as was the great Alpine-Himalayan mountain chain. There was also volcanic activity in the North Atlantic region, in East Africa, and in the Mediterranean region.	Most of the inland seas left the continents, and by the end of this period the continents had the same general outlines that they have today.	Grasslands were widespread. Mammals became the dominant land animals; primitive mammals disappeared. By this time cats, monkeys, whales, elephants, kangaroos, and birds were well established. The first anthropoid apes appeared. This period saw the modernization of flowering plants.
MESOZOIC *(from the Greek words* mesos, *meaning "middle" and* zoe, *meaning "life")*	CRETACEOUS (from the Latin word *creta,* meaning "chalk") 65 million to 136 million years ago	The Rocky Mountains of North America and the Andes of South America were formed as a result of the Laramide Disturbance.	Cretaceous seas covered most of Europe, much of Asia, and nearly half of North America. The Gulf of Mexico received nearly 11,000 feet of sediments during this period.	Flowering plants were common, as were giant sequoias. Sharks again became abundant. Snakes made their first appearance. The last of the dinosaurs disappeared from the land. Primitive mammals appeared.
	JURASSIC (named after the Jura Mountains) 136 million to 190 million years ago	A period of relative quiet. The Sierra Nevada Mountains were formed. Geosyncline downsinking took place along the western edges of both North and South America. In a way, the Jurassic was a stage-setting period for the great activity during the Cretaceous period.	Jurassic seas changed little from the Triassic. Seas continued to cover the western borders of North and South America.	Among plants, cycads, ferns, and scouring rushes flourished, and the first true pine trees appeared. Dinosaurs were numerous. The first lizards arose. Pterodactyls and feathered birds also appeared as did small mammals. Plesiosaurs, marine reptiles, became huge, measuring some 20 feet long.
	TRIASSIC (from the Latin word *trias,* meaning "three" and referring to a three-fold division of rock in southern Germany) 190 million to 225 million years ago	Extensive igneous activity took place during the Triassic, which includes the formation of the Palisades of New York and New Jersey and similar rock in South America, southern Africa, Australia, and Antarctica.	Seaways continued to cover the western edges of North and South America and some parts of Europe and Asia.	Because of cooler seas or for some other reason, many marine creatures such as sharks did poorly during this period. Thecodonts, ancestors of the dinosaurs, arose, as did turtles. Crocodiles also made their appearance along with marine reptiles such as ichthyosaurs.
PALEOZOIC *(from the Greek words* palaios, *meaning "ancient" and* zoe, *meaning "life")*	PERMIAN (named after the Province of Perm in the Ural Mountains of Russia) 225 million to 280 million years ago	The Appalachians south of New England were formed from the Appalachian Geosyncline. The Ural Mountains were also formed. Along the west coast of North America there was widespread volcanic activity. The reddish sedimentary strata of Monument Valley, Utah, were laid down during this time.	The western United States was still covered by shallow seas during this period. In other parts of the Northern Hemisphere seas were drying up and leaving vast deposits of salt and potash.	Conifers increased while the giant scouring rushes died out, Trilobites, some corals, and some amphibians also became extinct. A generally drying climate caused many plant and animal species to become extinct but favored the success of reptiles. Numerous varieties of reptiles have been discovered from this period.
	PENNSYLVANIAN	The Ouachita Mountains were altered many times	Some areas of the land sank, producing vast lakes,	About half of the world's workable coal was formed

280 million to 320 million years ago	In the Southern Hemisphere there was widespread glaciation.	were not so widespread as they were during the Mississippian Period.	resembling salamanders, ruled the land. The first reptiles arose during this period. Conifers and 40-foot-high scouring rushes were common.
MISSISSIPPIAN (named after the limestone area near the junction of the Mississippi and Missouri Rivers) 320 million to 345 million years ago	The Variscan Disturbance raised extensive mountains in Western Europe. The Ouachita Mountains of Oklahoma and Arkansas were formed.	Clear, shallow seas were still widespread in the Northern Hemisphere. The Appalachian Geosyncline, formed during the Cambrian Period, collected extensive deposits of sandy and muddy sediments from the rivers flowing down from the eastern land mass. Limestone was the most common sediment deposited in the shallow seas covering the mid-continent region.	Sharks were abundant during this period, and amphibians made their appearance as the major land animal. Hundred-foot-high scale trees grew on the edges of pools, shallow lakes, and swamps. Winged insects appeared for the first time, one with a wing-span of 29 inches (Meganeura).
DEVONIAN (named after Devon, England) 345 million to 395 million years ago	A land disturbance (called the Acadian Disturbance) raised high mountains in New England, Quebec, and Nova Scotia. The Kanimbla Disturbance raised mountains along the east coast of Australia.	Most of North America continued to be covered by shallow seas during most of the Devonian.	A bewildering variety of fishes arose during this period. Plants were plentiful and included giant tree ferns 40 feet high. Late in this period lobe-finned fishes began to establish themselves on the land.
SILURIAN (named after the Silures, an ancient tribe living in Wales) 395 million to 430 million years ago	There was much volcanic activity in Maine, New Brunswick, and eastern Quebec. Land disturbances (called the Caledonian Disturbance) gave rise to a 4,000-mile-long mountain range extending from Wales through Scandinavia and westward to northern Greenland.	Most of the present-day land area of the Northern Hemisphere was under water during this period. Extensive salt deposits, such as those of western New York and Michigan, were formed.	The trilobites began to decrease in numbers during this period. Eurypterids, or "water scorpions," were quite common. The first land plants — ferns and psilopsids — appeared, as did the first air-breathing animals.
ORDOVICIAN (named after an ancient Celtic tribe, the Ordovices, living in Wales) 430 million to 500 million years ago	Later during the Ordovician Period the crust of the Earth extending from Newfoundland to the Carolinas of the United States was affected by granitic intrusions, metamorphism, and folding, giving rise to mountains of this Taconic disturbance.	About 70 percent of the present-day Northern Hemisphere was flooded during this period.	This was a rich period for marine life. Trilobites were numerous, as were bryozoans, graptolites, cephalopods, and crinoids. Jawless fishes also arose. First vertebrates (fishes) appeared. Algae were dominant.
CAMBRIAN (Roman name for Wales) 500 million to 570 million years ago	In North America, Europe, and Asia great troughs in the land (called "geosynclines") were filling up with sediments. Near the end of the Paleozoic Era, this sedimentary "fill" was thrust up as mountain ranges, including the Rocky Mountains and Appalachians.	Shallow seas periodically advanced and withdrew over the land, covering much of the United States, Europe, Asia, Australia, and South America.	The shallow Cambrian seas abounded with many forms of life, including sponges, trilobites, brachiopods, graptolites, and other animals without backbones. Algae were dominant.
PRECAMBRIAN 570 million to 4,500 million years ago.	The Sun and planets were formed out of gas and dust. Earth went through a molten phase and developed a solid crust and a primitive atmosphere of methane, ammonia, and hydrogen.	Sometime during this era the seas formed. But these early seas and oceans did not have the shape of our seas and oceans of today.	The first living things may have come into being about 3,000 million years ago. Rare fossils of algae-like and fungilike plants have been discovered. Fossil imprints of jellyfish, worm burrows, and, recently, brachiopods have also been found.

Adapted, by permission, from *Discovering Rocks and Minerals*, by Roy A. Gallant and Christopher J. Schuberth. © 1967 by Doubleday & Company, Inc.

What We Can Learn from Rocks and Their Fossils

Let us take a fossil and its piece of rock as an example. The fossil is a kind that we can find in a quarry near Liverpool, in England.

In this quarry, the rocks are a reddish color, which tells us that the rock was made from a desert sand. At some time in the past, then, this place near Liverpool was a hot, sandy desert. If we look around, we might find a slab of this reddish rock that shows a change in the conditions long ago. On this slab we can see something which is very familiar. There are ripple marks on it, the same sort of marks we see on a wave-washed beach—but turned to stone. So the sand forming this slab of the rock was once part of a beach and, when the wind blew, the water rose up in waves and made these ripple marks.

Another slab of rock from this same quarry can show us something equally interesting. On the flat surface, where it has been broken out of the quarry, we may see the pitted marks of raindrops. If we can find several of these slabs and can work out their original position in the quarry, they will tell us the direction of the wind that blew the rain that made these pitted marks nearly 200 million years ago!

Not very far away from our quarry, we may come upon the footprints of a number of little animals. Some of these footprints are rather like a human hand: there are five fingers and one is bent back like a thumb. But if we find a trail of these footprints we may be very puzzled for the "thumbs" are on the outside of the print. When these little trails were first found scientists could not understand them. One even drew the animal walking with crossed legs so that its thumbs would be in the correct position! Later scientists realized that the fifth toe was not a thumb at all but a shorter outside toe that many reptiles have.

These footprints, then, were made by a little reptile. No one has found the bones of this reptile, but lots of footprints have been found and we have been able to work out much about the animal; where it lived and what it lived on, and therefore what it was looking for as it wandered about.

As well as these handlike footprints, we can find a number of much smaller footprints of little animals that apparently ran along in a lizardlike way. From other pieces of rock we can learn a little of the plants that grew in this sandy place.

In this way we can learn what it was like just outside Liverpool 200 million years ago: the plants that grew there, the animals that lived there and what the weather was like.

—William Elgin Swinton (1961)

AND LET THERE BE LIFE II

❄❄❄

As scientists study the fossil record, they are drawn back through time: to 100 million years ago when Cretaceous seas covered most of Europe and nearly half of North America; to 180 million years ago when reptiles, including the dinosaurs, ruled the land and when feathered birds and mammals first appeared; to 300 million years ago when vast swamp sprawled over much of the Northern Hemisphere and amphibians ruled the land; to 380 million years ago, the "Age of Fishes," before there were any land animals; to 550 million years ago when the Cambrian seas abounded with trilobites, brachiopods, and other animals without backbones; and still further back into the dark of the Precambrian, which dates from about 570 million years ago to the beginning of planet Earth. Biologists now think that the first life forms may have come into being about three thousand million years ago. But here the fossil evidence becomes difficult to interpret. There are fossil imprints of jellyfishes and worm burrows of the late Precambrian, and microfossil remnants of bacteria some three billion years old, but no such fossil remains ever are likely to be found of the precursors of those primitive organisms.

When scientists discover that they are on a dead-end street, they immediately search for alternate avenues that may lead to the same destination. Where the fossil record appears to end, biologists reorient their search for the beginnings of life, for that first matter that can be said to be "living." Inevitably, however, they must turn to scientists of other disciplines. According to the British biochemist J. D. Bernal, "the formulation of this problem is beyond the reach of any one scientist, for such a scientist would have to be at the same time a competent mathematician, physicist, and experienced organic chemist, he should have a very extensive knowledge of geology, geophysics, and geochemistry and besides all this, be absolutely at home in all biological disciplines." So in his search for the origins of life, one of the first things the interested biologist must do is find out from the astronomer, the geologist, and the geochemist their views of what primitive Earth may have been like early in the Precambrian.

According to the earth scientists, after Earth condensed from a sphere of gas and dust its gravitation caused its materials to pack more and more tightly around the core region. During such a process of compaction, and of radioactive heating, the planet would have heated up fairly rapidly to a temperature of about 1,200°K (about 2,000°F). Such heating would cause iron and other heavy materials to migrate toward the core region. Lighter-weight materials, such as the silicate rocks pre-

※ *This block of sandstone from New York's Catskill Mountains contains numerous fossil brachiopods of the Devonian Period that are some 400 million years old.* SCIENCE PHOTO/GRAPHICS, LTD.

sently forming Earth's crust, would tend to float in the soup of denser materials. During some such process of separation many gases would bubble out of solution and collect above the new planet as a primitive atmosphere. Among such gases would be large amounts of hydrogen (H), water vapor (H_2O), nitrogen (N_2), methane (CH_4), hydrogen sulfide (H_2S), and ammonia (NH_3).

As more and more water vapor collected in the atmosphere it would be cooled, condense out, and fall as rain. Because Earth's surface probably was still hot during this period, the new rains would vaporize on contact with the ground. But gradually as the crust cooled the torrential rains would begin to form pools that in time developed into local seas. Meanwhile, ultraviolet energy from the Sun would have broken down some of the complex gases, changing NH_3 into free hydrogen and molecules of nitrogen (N_2), CH_4 into carbon and hydrogen, and H_2O into hydrogen and oxygen. The free hydrogen was so light that most of it escaped Earth's gravitational grip. Many such reactions would have been taking place in that atmosphere that in no way resembled Earth's atmosphere today. So, if the earth scientists are correct, some 400 million years after our planet had developed a solid, cool crust, it accumulated its first seas and had an atmosphere made up mainly of methane, ammonia, and water vapor.

Chemists have shown that energy from the Sun, lightning, and other sources can cause those molecules to react and build up into more complex molecules of different substances. In the early 1950s, a young graduate student named Stanley Miller working at the University of Chicago, designed an experiment to find out what kinds of molecules might have been built up in Earth's primitive atmosphere.

Through a closed system of glass tubing Miller circulated a

mixture of hydrogen, methane, ammonia, and water vapor and then applied electric discharges to the gases as a substitute for the lightning in Earth's primitive atmosphere. The water vapor condensed as "rain," and the other gases dissolved in the water. A week later Miller drew off some of the solution and examined it. A number of complex molecules had been built up, molecules known to be essential to all living things. Among those molecules were amino acids, which are the building blocks of proteins. But such relatively simple molecules were a far cry from anything that we could call "living." Larger and far more complex molecules were needed. About 95 percent of all living matter, by the way, is composed of the four elements hydrogen, carbon, nitrogen, and oxygen.

Such molecules gradually would have been built up as amino acids, and other molecules were washed out of the atmosphere by rain and fell on warm rock surfaces where they would have combined as proteinlike compounds. Eventually they would have been washed into the newly forming seas along with salts and other materials dissolved from the rock crust, creating Darwin's "warm little pond." At this stage a kind of chemical natural selection would have taken place in that primordial broth. Certain molecules that were stable and resisted being broken down would remain, or be selected *for*. But certain other molecules, less stable in their makeup at the existing temperatures, would be broken down, or selected *against*. And so we can imagine such a chemical state of affairs existing some 3 to 4 billion years ago.

But how could such nonliving molecules, no matter how complex, bridge that immense gap and become collections of a substance that we can term "living"? Here we may be setting a semantic trap for ourselves by taking an either-or (living *versus* nonliving) view of things. Such a view implies that

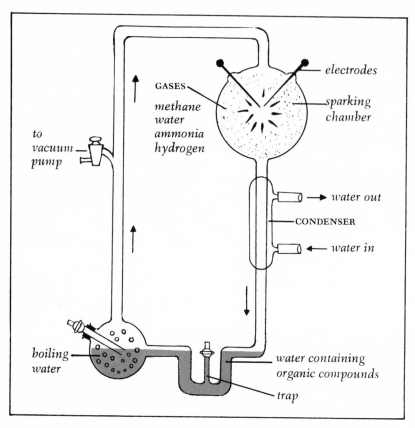

※ The apparatus Miller used in his experiments in the synthesis of amino acids in simulated primitive Earth conditions. SCIENCE PHOTO/ GRAPHICS, LTD.

※ There are only about 20 amino acids commonly occurring in living matter. The simplest one is glycine, shown here. It consists of two atoms of carbon, two of oxygen, five of hydrogen, and one of nitrogen. SCIENCE PHOTO/GRAPHICS, LTD.

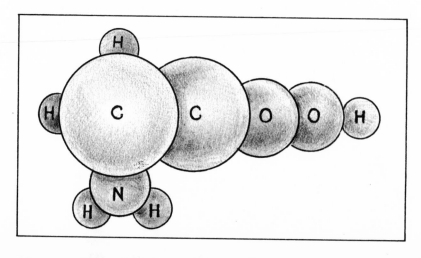

there is nothing in between. Actually, we should be speaking of a continuum of structures ranging from elements to simple molecules to increasingly complex aggregates of molecules and eventually to molecular systems that can be termed "living."

The smallest unit of living material recognized by biologists is the cell. And on the biological scale of things, the difference between the molecules we have been talking about so far and the cell can be compared to the difference between a crystal in all its simplicity and the Grand Canyon in all its complexity. If, indeed, complex molecules in Earth's primitive environment developed into increasingly complex structures and eventually evolved into the first cells, the process probably took at least a billion years. The immensity of such a time span is impossible for the mind to grasp. If we let one year be represented by the thickness of a page of this book, then a billion years would be represented by a stack of books (minus their covers) fifty miles high!

Oparin has suggested that the next stage in chemical evolution might have been the buildup of complex molecular assemblages called "coacervates" (from the Latin *acervatus,* meaning "clustered"). Several individual protein particles are known to clump and form a coacervate droplet. Because the protein molecules have an electric charge, the surrounding water molecules are kept at a certain distance and form a neat shell around the protein cluster. The shell acts as a sac that encloses the protein particles in the same way that the membrane envelope of a cell encloses the contents of the cell. A coacervate droplet, then, has an internal environment (its own contents) and an external environment (the surrounding water). However, the membranelike shell of a coacervate droplet is not an impenetrable barrier. The droplet can attract certain complex molecules from the outside environment and incorporate them into its own internal environment. But these molecules from the outside must be exactly the right shape so that they can fit into the neat arrangement of the molecules making up the droplet itself, like perfectly fitting pieces of a jig-saw puzzle. In other words, certain kinds of complex molecules moving about in a disorderly fashion in the outside environment are taken in and added to a highly ordered arrangement of molecules. Even though such droplets are "nonliving," (that trap again!) we can describe their process of becoming larger and more complex as "growth."

According to Oparin, there must have been many different kinds of coacervate droplets in Earth's primitive seas, some more stable than others. Those that were selected for and survived would tend to be better organized and surrounded by plenty of "nutrient" molecules that could be incorporated into the droplets for growth. Oparin pictures the more chemically successful droplets growing to such large size that they became unstable and broke into smaller droplets like themselves. These small droplets in turn took in nutrients from the outside and grew in a process of "reproduction." Whether you call coacervate droplets living or nonliving depends on your particular bias in defining "life." Oparin has said, "there is no *fundamental* difference between a living organism and lifeless matter." Like cells making up your body, coacervate droplets take in nutrients from the outside, they have a protective membrane, they grow, and they can reproduce more of their kind. Do they qualify as living matter or not?

The kinds of coacervate droplets we have been talking about—*pre*biological cells as we might call them—relied for growth and reproduction on certain complex molecules in the outside environment. Such prebiological cells could not keep on reproducing endlessly. Eventually they would use up most or all of the nutrient molecules available in the outside environment. Growth and reproduction would then slow down accordingly and eventually stop. It would seem that an alternative means of getting nutrients for growth would have been necessary for prebiological cells to survive.

Among the many different kinds of prebiological cells, we can imagine some able to take in very simple molecules from the outside environment. These would not be ready-made nutrients but their raw materials, which would be assembled into complex nutrient molecules once inside the cell. Such simple raw-material molecules would tend to be more numerous than the ready-made nutrient molecules. So while the first prebiological cells took in ready-made food from the outside environment, there were others that took in simpler substances and out of those substances made their own food. Such "organisms" would have an obvious edge over their competitors. An example of such organisms today are the many different kinds of green plants that depend only on the raw materials carbon dioxide and water vapor from the air and the energy of sunlight to make their own complex food (glucose, a sugar).

During a period of millions of years those first prebiological cells must have become increasingly more efficient in making their own food out of basic raw materials in the external environment. And as they did, they evolved into the first biological, or living, cells. Microfossils of such living matter, described as algaelike, have been dated at about 3.5 billion years old. At the present time, however, the many details of their chemical evolution from those first complex molecules containing oxygen, carbon, hydrogen, and nitrogen are unknown. Because there is such an immense gulf between the most complex prebiological cells and the simplest biological cells, perhaps we shall never fill in the details of how those extremes were linked, except in the broadest of outlines. But that may be taking a needlessly pessimistic view. According to the biochemist Cyril Ponnamperuma: "There is no reason to doubt that we shall rediscover one by one the physical and chemical conditions that once determined and directed the course of chemical evolution. We may even reproduce the intermediate steps in the laboratory." In any case, evidence presently at hand suggests that prebiological cells did become increasingly efficient in making their own food and then using it for growth and reproduction.

As they did, according to this line of reasoning, they caused Earth's atmosphere to evolve in an important way. As they combined carbon dioxide with water in the presence of sunlight in the process called *photosynthesis,* they would have given off free oxygen as a by-product:

$$CO_2 + H_2O \longrightarrow [CH_2O] + H_2O + O_2 \uparrow$$

CARBON   WATER   GLUCOSE   WATER   OXYGEN
DIOXIDE VAPOR

The accumulating supply of free oxygen in the atmosphere would then have acted on the remaining methane by breaking it down and converting it into carbon dioxide and water vapor. It also would have broken down ammonia and converted it into free nitrogen and water vapor. Eventually, such reactions would have led to our present atmosphere, which is about 78 percent nitrogen, 21 percent oxygen, and 1 percent carbon dioxide, neon, argon, and several other gases.

If you could pin down a scientist who has devoted most of his career to the study of the origins of life to a specific time when "life" began, he would probably single out that period when Earth's atmosphere changed most recently, when it became oxygen-rich because of cells able to carry out photosynthesis—possibly as long ago as 3 billion years.

THE OLDEST KNOWN FOSSILS (all from the Precambrian Era)

AGE	KIND AND LOCATION
900 million years	Microscopic plant organisms found in Bitter Springs, Australia. Thirty different species identified, 14 of which resemble algae living today.
1.6 to 2.0 billion years	Microscopic algae found in rock along the northern shore of Lake Superior in Ontario. Twelve species of these microscopic plants have been identified; also some rod-shaped bacteria.
3.1 billion years	Microscopic bacterialike organisms found near Fig Tree, South Africa. Similar to present-day blue-green algae and possibly able to carry on photosynthesis.
3.4 to 3.6 billion years	Microscopic organisms similar to those found near Fig Tree have been found in Swaziland, Africa, and are the oldest known fossils of once living organisms.

Although there are glaring omissions in the biological version of Genesis, nearly all biologists agree that some such broad outline like the one described here seems highly likely. As time passes, laboratory experiments, such as those done by Oparin, Miller, and many others, confirm that broad outline as they keep supplying new details. Most biologists also agree that given the right conditions, the right blend of matter and energy, life of some sort is bound to come into being due to natural causes, not only on Earth but elsewhere in the Universe.

In the 1800s the Irish chemist John Tyndall reasoned that if every part of a living organism could be broken down chemically into the basic elements, then the reverse process should also hold true: that is, those same parts could be synthesized, or built up, from elemental matter. In 1924, Oparin, the father of modern studies of the origins of life, summarized the process in these words:

> At first there were the simple solutions of organic substances, the behavior of which was governed by the properties of their component atoms and the arrangement of those atoms in the molecular structure. But gradually, as the result of growth and increased complexity of the molecules, new colloidal-chemical order was imposed on the more simple organic chemical relations. These newer properties were determined by the spatial arrangement and mutual relationship of the molecules. . . . In this process biological orderliness already comes into prominence. Competitive speed of growth, struggle for existence and, finally, natural selection determined such a form of material organization which is characteristic of living things of the present time.

According to Ponnamperuma, "What we are then doing is an inquiry, not an attempt to prove or disprove, rather a search to find out how the sequence of events in the Universe led to the first life." This view, of course, is entirely materialistic: nonliving matter over immense time evolves into living matter without the aid of supernatural powers. And it is a view that is at swords' points with the creationists, those who believe that all living things were created by a supernatural force some 6,000 years ago and that species do not change with time.

It is not my purpose here to take sides, but to present both points of view and to trace their development over the ages. This is the crux of the matter: *how those points of view originated and evolved and how they are changing today in the light of new discoveries.*

When we look about us, it is difficult not to be impressed by the sheer range of life forms, which biologists call *diversity.* In their attempts to catalog all the different kinds of living things on Earth, so far biologists have counted about 1,200,000 species of animals and nearly 500,000 species of plants. Equally impressive is the fact that each year another 15,000 new species are added to the lists. But even more impressive, if we include all the species that have existed in the past but are now extinct, we are overwhelmed by the diversity of life. Biologists now estimate that more than 99 percent of all of the species that have ever lived on Earth are now extinct!

During Earth's history life has invaded every nook and cranny. There are bacteria that live in hot springs with temperatures above the boiling point. There are plants that live on mountain tops where the temperature is always below freezing. There are air-breathing mammals, such as whales, that live under water. There are ants and spiders and people and lobsters and there are birds galore.

DIVERSITY IN SIZE

Organism	Relative Size
Blue whale (100 feet)	10,000,000
Elephant	1,100,000
Human (Man)	567,000
Dog	200,000
Pigeon	125,000
Lobster	100,000
Starfish	58,000
Grasshopper	13,000
Ameba	167
Spore (3 microns)	1

The inquiring mind of the scientist asks: How did life flower into such bewildering and splendid variety?

6

THE EVIDENCE
FOR EVOLUTION

*Is evolution a theory, a system, or a hypothesis?
It is much more—it is a general postulate to
which all theories, all hypotheses, all systems
must henceforward bow and which they must
satisfy in order to be thinkable and true. Evolution is a light which illuminates all facts, a
trajectory which all lines of thought must follow.*

—Pierre Teilhard de Chardin (1881–1955)

ENTER DARWIN

When the book was published on November 24, 1859,
it set off a tidal wave of shock, anger, and protest that was
felt around the world. Leading scientists and members of the
clergy alike were stunned, for the book boldly challenged that
citadel of truth and authority for nearly 2,000 years, the Bible.

The book argued that living species of animals and plants
change biologically over periods of millions of years as the environment changes. By the mid-1800s geologists had proven
beyond doubt that Earth's surface is in a continual state of

change. What is now land was once covered by vast inland seas. Long periods of cold had gripped parts of Europe and North America and covered them with great ice sheets, parts of that land beneath once having been swamps. Tropical forests could change into deserts, and sections of the ocean floor could be thrust up as mountains. By the 1830s the influential English geologist Charles Lyell had "officially" turned the biblical clock of creation back millions of years. Even earlier the Scottish geologist James Hutton had recognized the immensity of time when he declared that geologically there was "no vestige of a beginning and no prospect of an end."

The book held that in the face of such changes in the environment many species of animals and plants would not be able to cope with new and severe conditions and would perish, and once extinct, they could never again return. From time to time, however, certain particularly well-fit individuals of some species managed to cope with environmental change and survived. In some small but important way those individuals were different from their less fit companions who perished. They survived and passed on to their offspring that small but important difference. Over millions of years, said the book's author, many such small changes taking place within a species gradually caused the species to change in significant ways in a process called evolution. In short, species evolve.

❦❦❦❦❦❦❦❦❦❦❦❦❦❦❦❦❦❦❦❦❦❦❦❦❦❦❦❦❦❦❦❦❦❦❦

A tree and a squirrel have not always been what they are now. They have *become* so, and how they became so is essential to understanding what they are. The tree grew from a seed; the squirrel developed from a zygote in its mother's uterus. Understanding cannot stop there. It must follow the seed and the zygote back and back through the generations to times when there were no seeds or zygotes, no trees or squirrels. The long

process of becoming that is evolution yields the most profound
understanding of the organism that exists today.
—George Gaylord Simpson (1957)

※※※

At the time, most scholars and clergymen alike believed that
species never change. Dogs had always been exactly the same,
as had roses, snails, and, of course, man. Man had remained
the same since the time God had created Adam out of dust.
It was God who created each and every species according to
His divine plan, His design, and a new species could not possibly arise unless He created it.

Some scientists of the 1800s also refused to accept the fossil
evidence that species become extinct. They believed that every
species ever "created" still inhabited the planet. One American
scientist held this belief so stubbornly that he insisted that mas-
todons, whose fossil bones he knew about, still secretly roamed
parts of North America. "Such is the economy of nature," he
wrote, "that no instance can be produced of her having per-
mitted any one race of her animals to become extinct; of her
having formed any link in her great work so weak as to be
broken." The scientist was a man named Thomas Jefferson.
Many feel that he was more successful as a politician than as
a biologist.

Such was the conflict touched off by the idea of evolution
published in that controversial book with the long title, *The
Origin of Species by Means of Natural Selection, or the Preservation of Favoured Races in the Struggle for Life.* Its author
was a fifty-year-old English country gentleman named Charles
Robert Darwin. People tended to accept Darwin's idea about
evolution completely or not at all. For example, when *The
Origin of Species* was published, one scientist said that in all

ON

THE ORIGIN OF SPECIES

BY MEANS OF NATURAL SELECTION,

OR THE

PRESERVATION OF FAVOURED RACES IN THE STRUGGLE
FOR LIFE.

BY CHARLES DARWIN, M.A.,

FELLOW OF THE ROYAL, GEOLOGICAL, LINNÆAN, ETC., SOCIETIES;
AUTHOR OF 'JOURNAL OF RESEARCHES DURING H. M. S. BEAGLE'S VOYAGE
ROUND THE WORLD.'

LONDON:
JOHN MURRAY, ALBEMARLE STREET.
1859.

The right of Translation is reserved.

Title page of the original edition of The Origin of Species.

"fairness" he would read it, "but I will never believe it." The famous American scientist Louis Agassiz was enraged by Darwin's ideas and during the 1860s began a series of lectures to point out the dangers of evolution theory to the American people.

On the day Darwin's book was published, all 1,250 copies were sold and a new printing was ordered. After he had delivered his manuscript to the publisher for the first printing, Darwin had sat back in dread, waiting for the outburst he knew would soon come. He was a gentle soul and would avoid conflict at nearly any cost, so when the intellectual storm broke, as he knew it would, he was deeply disturbed. And the storm raged for years. However, today the vast majority of scientists accept as fact the idea of evolution through natural selection. So overwhelming is the evidence in support of it that they regard evolution as one of the fundamental principles of biology. But the creationists still refuse to accept any part of evolution, saying that the fossil record actually disproves it and maintaining a belief that the orderliness in nature could never have come about by natural means or chance. It required the creative hand of a designer, of God.

❦❦❦

EARLIER EVOLUTIONISTS

❦❦❦

The idea that species evolve along with Earth itself was not new with Darwin. Nearly a hundred years earlier the highly influential French scientist George L. de Buffon had maintained that changes in Earth's physical environment brought about structural changes in plants and animals, changes that were in some way, unknown at the time, passed on from parents to offspring. He based his thinking partly on the fact that many animals have useless parts, such as the tailbone in human beings. Buffon seems to have been the first European Christian openly to contradict the biblical date of creation of 4004 B.C. by saying that life had existed for millions of years. Also in the 1700s, Darwin's grandfather, Erasmus Darwin, suggested that millions of years ago there had been a primitive parent organism that had given rise to all the living things about us today. Over those millions of years, he said, the countless offspring of the original parent kept changing, improving by becoming more fit and evolving into forms more and more like today's organisms. In 1794 he wrote: "Would it be too bold to imagine that in the great length of time since the earth began to exist perhaps millions of ages before the history of mankind . . . all warm-blooded animals have arisen from one living filament?"

The French biologist Jean Baptiste de Lamarck was the first to come up with a full-fledged theory of evolution. In 1809, the year Darwin was born, Lamarck proposed that evolution takes place as individual animals and plants acquire new and beneficial characters, in effect, because they try harder! The newly acquired character—a longer reach, a faster gait, a keener nose—would then be passed on from parent to offspring.

As the diagram shows, over a period of three generations, short-antlered deer could "evolve" into long-antlered animals. At first (top) all members of the species have short antlers. Because longer antlers are more useful as a means of protection, the individuals acquire longer antlers through intensive use. Individuals of the next generation (middle) would inherit the longer antlers from their parents. In turn, they would increase their antler length and pass on the still greater length to their offspring (bottom), and so on until the antlers reach the "most useful" length. Lamarck viewed evolution as a process of "increasing perfection" of individual organisms, but it was a hypothesis that was doomed to fail.

Darwin was just seventeen and a first-year medical student when he heard about Lamarck's views on evolution. Later, Darwin was to recall that he "listened in silent astonishment, and as far as I can judge, without any effect on my mind. I had previously read the [book on evolution written by] my grandfather, in which similar views are maintained, but without producing any effect on me."

At first, this total lack of interest in evolution may seem to be in glaring contradiction to Darwin's most intense interest in later life. We find a clue to Darwin as a scientist and to Darwin's early uninterest in evolution in a comment he made in later life about his grandfather's book: "I was much disappointed [in it], the proportion of speculation being so large to the facts given." Darwin hungered for hard evidence gained through observation, evidence that would buttress a lofty idea or utterly demolish it. Later, he was to spend nearly fifty years painstakingly gathering mountains of evidence and building his own idea of evolution through natural selection.

❧❧❧

CATASTROPHISM
AND SPECIAL CREATION

❧❧❧

During Darwin's youth geologists were hard put to explain why the fossils found in one layer of rock were so strikingly different from the fossils found in rock layers of earlier and later ages. The fossil record seemed to suggest that at one period in Earth's history certain kinds of animals and

❆ *According to Lamarckian evolution, antlers, for example, would grow longer with use in the individual animal's lifetime for the "purpose" of improving defense against predators. So increased antler length was presumed to be an acquired characteristic that was passed on from parent to offspring* COURTESY: JOHN WILEY & SONS, INC.

plants existed, but then mysteriously died out as if some deathly plague had swept the land. Then in the overlying, younger rock layer a different assemblage of fossils would be found. Where did these new plants and animals come from? They too were to become extinct in later ages, for in still more recent rock layers not a trace of them was to be found. Entirely different species took their place. Also, each new layering of rock contained fossils of animals that more closely resembled animals that roam the planet now.

How could such observations be accounted for? When Darwin was still a youth, Cuvier's catastrophism seemed to be the answer: "The dislocation and overturning of older [rock] strata show without any doubt," Cuvier wrote, "that the causes which brought them into the position which they now occupy were sudden and violent. . . . The evidence of those great and terrible events are everywhere to be clearly seen by anyone who knows how to read the record of the rocks."

Those scientists who accepted catastrophism also tended to accept as part of the package the idea of the "special creation" of new species. How else could the new tide of life that followed each mass destruction envisioned by Cuvier be accounted for? After each catastrophe, they reasoned, God created a whole new assemblage of animals and plants to replace those He had created earlier but which He then had desroyed during the most recent catastrophe. The Divine Creator, then, for reasons unknowable to man, wrought wholesale destruction on living organisms and then replaced them with new species.

The ideas of catastrophism and special creation went hand in hand, seeming to explain everything about the origin of new species and the neatly layered fossil record simply and thoroughly. Catastrophism was based on hard geological evidence and was entirely compatible with the biblical theory of creation. One of the more outspoken creationists of the time was the English clergyman William Paley. His book, *Natural Theology*, published in 1802, was required reading for naturalists and divinity students alike. Darwin had to read it while he was studying for the ministry at Cambridge, and it made a very strong impression on him at the time.

Paley's argument went like this: Every living insect, fish, and plant is cleverly adapted to its environment, from those insects and other animals whose protective coloring helps hide them from predators, to the streamlined bodies of fishes, to certain plants able to grow on brick walls or under water. The adaptations that so cleverly fit each species of plant and animal to its environment could not have come about by accident, Paley argued. Surely they are the design of a superior intelligence. "Design must have had a designer," he reasoned. "That designer must have been a person. That person is God." Paley was sure that God had designed all of those complex adaptations in order to show His wisdom "scientifically."

Lyell could not bring himself to accept the catastrophism-creationism package. He saw more merit in the idea that species died out gradually as their individual members became less and less fit for survival due to unfavorable changes in the environment. He did not try to offer an explanation of how new species arose. And where man's origin and destiny as a species were concerned, Lyell turned to the Bible. He believed that Earth had always had living things on it, and that there never had been a time when nonliving things changed into primitive life forms. He also believed that there would always be geological change accompanied by the extinction of some species and the coming into being of others.

There is no doubt that Lyell had a profound influence on young Darwin. At once he was a devout Christian who re-

✻ The Canadian Rockies ptarmigan (note female with five young in foreground) is an example of a species that has adapted well to its environment, in this case through protective coloration. COURTESY: THE AMERICAN MUSEUM OF NATURAL HISTORY, PHOTO BY THE AUTHOR

spected the Bible as a historical document, and he was a scientist who refused to dodge conclusions based on hard evidence. Nothing could convince Lyell that sudden geological upheavals —Cuvier's catastrophes—had ever occurred. Instead he looked to gradual change, or *uniformitarianism*, as such change is called by geologists. "No causes whatever have from the earliest time to which we can look back, to the present, ever acted but those now acting and they have never acted with different degrees of energy from which they now exert."

VOYAGE
OF H.M.S. BEAGLE

"On returning home from my short geological tour in North Wales," Darwin wrote, "I found a letter from Henslow, informing me that a Captain FitzRoy was willing to give up part of his own cabin to any young man who would volunteer to go with him without pay as naturalist [on a five-year, around-the-world] voyage of H.M.S. *Beagle*."

"I was instantly eager to accept the offer," Darwin recalled later, and he did. FitzRoy was a brilliant but strange young man. He was deeply religious, with a strong sense of duty to his fellow man. At the age of 23, only 3 years Darwin's senior, he had been given command of the *Beagle*, a 240-ton warship fitted out for surveying. The purpose of the surveying voyage was to chart the coasts of South America, and FitzRoy wanted a ship's naturalist along for two reasons. First, on a previous surveying voyage FitzRoy had suspected that some of the South American regions he had explored contained valuable mineral deposits, and he wanted someone with a knowledge of geology to inspect them. Second, during Darwin's interview with Fitz-Roy, the captain made it perfectly clear that he believed in every word of the Bible and that he was convinced beyond a doubt that Darwin's observations of plants, animals, and fossils would prove once and for all the "scientific" truth of the Book of Genesis.

At the time, Darwin had no reason to challenge FitzRoy's views and felt that the captain probably was right in his expectations of what Darwin would find. After all, FitzRoy's views were those of the Church of England, the church Darwin was to serve on his return home. At this time, Darwin did not in the least look on himself as a "scientist," but as an amateur naturalist. On December 27, 1831, the *Beagle* put to sea and "a new chapter in the history of science began," as Sir Gavin de Beer has put it. For it was during that long voyage that Darwin was to work out in broad outline his own ideas about the ways in which Earth's crustal rock and the life it supports have evolved.

At the Cape Verde Islands Darwin was fascinated by the behavior of cuttlefish stranded on the beach at low tide. In self-defense they would squirt water at any intruder. Darwin made a note that the cuttlefish invariably seemed to have a very good aim. Although an isolated observation, this was to become one of many thousands which, when added together, had a very important meaning: how species are adapted to their environment. Such adaptations may take the form of protective coloration in birds and insects, or the ability of desert cactus to store water. Those individuals able to protect themselves successfully survived and produced offspring similarly able to protect themselves well, since they inherited that ability from their parents. Those that could not protect themselves well usually did not live long enough to produce offspring. Here was the first glimmering of an idea that later was to develop into the theory of natural selection. But at this stage of the voyage Darwin was not building grand theories. Like a child let loose in a bakery, he was hungrily gobbling up everything he could reach. The difficult and painful process of digestion was to come later.

In the fall of 1832 the *Beagle* stopped at Bahía Blanca, about two-thirds of the way down the east coast of South America. It was here that Darwin made his first important discovery during the voyage. What he found confused him because it did not seem to agree with certain accounts in the Book of Genesis. He unearthed the fossilized head of a large animal encrusted in soft sedimentary rock. "It took me nearly three hours to get it out," he wrote. "As far as I am able to judge, it is [related] to the Rhinocerous."

There was also a huge jawbone that still had one tooth. When Darwin brought his prizes back to the ship and invited the captain to examine them, FitzRoy read into them exactly what he wanted and had expected Darwin to prove during the voyage—scientific proof of Genesis. FitzRoy said that obviously the bones belonged to huge animals that for some reason did not manage to get aboard Noah's ark in time to be saved from the flood. Darwin said nothing.

The skull he had found was later recognized as part of a *Toxodon*, an animal that became extinct about 2 million years ago and resembled a hippopotamus but belonged to the rodent family. The jawbone was subsequently identified as belonging to another extinct giant, the *Megatherium*, which had long, curved claws and was related to the sloth.

On return visits to the site, Darwin uncovered seven more fossil bones of giant extinct animals. He also found the remains

✺ *The reconstructed skeleton of* Megatherium.

of many smaller species that had become extinct. Darwin could not drive one important thought from his mind: all of the extinct giants that he had unearthed closely resembled living animals he had been observing day by day. *Toxodon*, for instance, resembled a living South American rodent known as capybara, which is about the size of a big collie. *Megatherium*, with its great claws, resembled the much smaller South American sloths living today, only some three feet high. Also there was a huge armadillolike animal among his fossil finds, a giant relative of armadillos living today.

Darwin marveled over the close relationships between the dead and the living. He had no doubts that one day these likenesses between species of the past and the present would "throw more light on the appearance of organic beings on earth and their disappearance from it."

As time passed and Darwin brought more and more fossils aboard, he found it increasingly difficult to accept FitzRoy's easy answers to questions posed by the fossils. For instance, one time Darwin challenged FitzRoy to defend the flood and Noah's ark. Try to picture, Darwin said, how large an ark would have to be to hold two Toxodons, two Megatherians, and two of the many other giant animals as large as elephants.

FitzRoy's answer was that some animals, for reasons known only to God, did not get aboard the ark and drowned in the flood. But Darwin wanted to know how FitzRoy could be so sure that the animals left behind were drowned. After all, Darwin argued, fossil seashells that are now part of the coastal rock were evidence that the land had once been under the sea and had later risen. How else could shells have been deposited there? FitzRoy's answer was that the land had not risen at all. The bones of Darwin's fossil animals, and fossil seashells found on the land today, showed beyond a doubt that the sea had risen in a gigantic flood that had drowned all the animals left behind. So FitzRoy matched Darwin point for point.

Darwin's careful study of the geology of the Patagonian coast of South America showed him that the east coast of that land, inland to an average distance of 200 miles, had in ages past been part of the sea floor. Wherever he examined the face of a cliff, he found fossil layers of marine animals. Some were only 100 or so feet beneath the topmost layer. Others were beneath nearly 1,000 feet of overlying rock.

Some time in the past those living marine animals had died and drifted to the sea floor. Ever so slowly, their remains were covered by sands, clays, and other materials washed off the land. Century after century more sediments accumulated, piling ever higher above the shells. Next, forces within Earth caused these great sediment banks to heave up out of the sea as hard rock. This was the unmistakable sequence of events that Darwin could read in the fossil record preserved in the rocks of Patagonia.

FitzRoy was becoming more and more disappointed in Darwin. The truth was to be found in Genesis, FitzRoy maintained, not in wild ideas from scattered pieces of rock and bones. Darwin no longer accepted *any* authority. He had become convinced that truth about the history of life on this planet could be found only if man patiently probed back into geological time by learning to read the fossil record.

The great earthquake of 1835 that shook the South American coast around Concepción settled the argument between Darwin and FitzRoy about the Noachian flood waters covering the land and so accounting for marine fossils found on land. Darwin recounted that when the two went ashore to examine the widespread damage they found:

the whole coast was strewn over with timber and furniture as if a thousand ships had been wrecked. . . . The store-houses at Talcahuano had been burst open, and great bags of cotton and other valuable merchandise were scattered on the shore. During my walk, I observed that numerous fragments of rock, which, from the marine productions adhering to them, must recently have been lying in deep water, had been cast up high on the beach. One of these was six feet long, three broad, and two thick. . . . There can be no doubt that the land round the Bay of Concepción was upraised two or three feet.

Here was proof for FitzRoy that the land can and does rise out of the sea. Later, at the island of Santa María, about thirty miles from Concepción, FitzRoy himself observed beds of mussel shells ten feet above the high-water mark. Before the quake, even at low tide, fishermen had to dive to reach those mussel beds. FitzRoy could not deny that here the land had risen.

In the fall of 1835, the *Beagle* stopped at the Galápagos Islands, about 500 miles off the coast of Ecuador. These volcanic islands had boiled up out of the sea floor more that 100 million years ago. During his time ashore Darwin counted 26 species of land birds. That in itself was not important, but the fact that 25 of those species were unknown elsewhere in the world interested him very much.

Although the idea of natural selection did not strike Darwin in full force until years later, the idea of evolution did come to him at the Galápagos. On each island he was collecting and identifying the different species of birds. Among them were thirteen species of finches. Darwin kept all of the birds collected on James Island in one bag, those collected on Chatham Island in another bag, and so on. In this way he could tell just where he had collected each specimen.

As he began to study the finches, he noticed that some were

black and others brownish. Although somewhat different in color, still they all looked rather alike: all had shortish tails and similarly shaped bodies, built the same kinds of nests, and laid the same number and same color eggs. They also generally resembled the finches found on the South American mainland. There was, however, a striking difference among the beaks of the Galápagos finches. They could be arranged, or graded, from a stubby, parrotlike beak at one extreme to a long thin beak at the other extreme.

❧ Beak structure of four species of Galápagos finches studied by Darwin. SCIENCE PHOTO/GRAPHICS, LTD.

Those finches with the heavy, parrotlike beaks could crack tough nuts and crush smaller seeds. The beak structures of those finches adapted them to a certain kind of diet. The finches with long, pointed beaks could not crack nuts; these finches were adapted to a different kind of diet that consisted of soft fruits and flowers. Still others had beaks adapted for catching insects on the wing or for probing into the cracks of bark in search of insects. Darwin marveled over this difference in beak structure among his community of finches. But he had not yet discovered the most remarkable thing about these birds.

"To my astonishment," he later recalled, "I discovered that all the finches from Charles Island belonged to one species and [had the same shape beak]; all from Albemarle Island belonged to another species [and had the same shape beak]; and all from James and Chatham Islands to still other species."

What did it all mean? Could it be that here on these islands remote "both in space and time we seem to be brought somewhat nearer to that great fact—that mystery of mysteries—the first appearance of new beings on this Earth?"

Darwin imagined a time in the past when the islands of the Galápagos had just risen out of the sea. There was nothing but the cooling black lavas. Eventually, however, land birds from the mainland found their way to the islands. Seeds from their droppings took hold in the primitive soil forming on the rock, and eventually several species from the mainland migrated to and inhabited the islands.

Darwin pictured one species of finch that was the original ancestor of the thirteen species he had collected. As plant life spread over each of the islands, the various species of animals settling there either were adapted to the particular environment of a particular island or they were not. Those that were sufficiently well adapted were successful and remained. Darwin further imagined that succeeding generations of offspring changed ever so slightly, those individuals best adapted having an edge over those less well adapted.

Since the environment on each island is different from the environment on every other island in the Galápagos group, a species settling on one island would evolve differently from others of its members which settled on a different island. Although the finches had all evolved from a common finch ancestor, those original ancestors no longer survived. For some reason we shall probably never know, they were unable to adapt to some new condition in the environment. In the same way, those giants whose fossil bones Darwin had found in the rock near Bahía Blanca had failed to survive.

And so the original ancestors of the Galápagos finches had evolved from still more ancient ancestors. The more ancient the ancestor, the less it resembled the living species today. And so in some marvelous but mysterious way, life could be traced back in time, back along an unbroken chain of living things, back to Earth's beginning as a planet. Here was that "mystery of mysteries—the first appearance of new beings on this Earth."

The idea was terribly hazy, and Darwin could not begin to imagine even the biggest links in that chain of life spanning geologic time. But he felt that he was onto something very important. He realized that if he were right, many people would resent him bitterly. They would have to change their thinking about man and give up beliefs that had been held for centuries. The biblical story of Adam and Eve, for instance, would have to be looked on as only myth, a story invented by man to account for man.

At the Keeling Islands in the Indian Ocean, Darwin described another example of a marvel in adaptation—a large crab that lived on a diet of coconut meat:

[It] is very common on all parts of the dry land. The front pair of legs end in very strong and heavy pincers. It would at first be thought quite impossible for a crab to open a strong cocoanut covered with the husk . . . but the crab begins by tearing the husk, fibre by fibre, and always from the end under which the three eye-holes are. When this is done, the crab begins hammering with its heavy claws on one of the eye-holes 'till an opening is made. Then turning round its body, by the aid of its smaller legs, the crab digs out the white meat. I think this is as curious a case of instinct as ever I heard of, and likewise of adaption in structure between two objects so different from each other in the scheme of nature as a crab and a cocoanut tree.

❊❊❊

A TIME
FOR DECISION

❊❊❊

On October 2, 1836, the *Beagle* docked at Falmouth. Darwin left her for the last time and began a new chapter in his life. Over the next twenty years he worked doggedly on his theory of evolution through natural selection, tirelessly collecting ever more evidence and, in a way, delaying the day when he would have to write it all down for others to read. Something in him wanted to be "safe" from criticism, but deep down he knew there was no such safety. From 1854 on Darwin devoted all his time to arranging his masses of notes on how species change and observing and experimenting with domestic animals to find out what more he could learn about selection. He interviewed breeders of pigeons, cattle, dogs, sheep, and goldfish. He experimented with and studied earthworms, bees, moths, butterflies, orchids and other plants.

During his interviews with expert breeders of domestic animals and plants, several things were made clear to Darwin. For instance, certain characteristics of an animal could be passed on from parent to offspring. A dairyman selected from all the rest those few cows that gave the most milk. He then mated those cows with his prize bull. By selecting out of each new generation of cows those that gave the most milk and then by breeding those cows only, the dairyman would eventually have a herd of cows that gave much more milk than a herd consisting of an arbitrary mixture of good milk cows and poor milk cows.

Pigeon breeders, rose breeders, and vegetable growers alike had clearly shown that a species could be made to change in dramatic ways by selective breeding. The fact of selection could not be denied. "I soon perceived that selection was the keystone of man's success in making useful races of animals and plants. But how selection could be applied to organisms living in a state of nature remained for some time a mystery to me," Darwin wrote.

The creationists maintained that because all new species are created by God, therefore they are "perfect" and completely adapted to the environment at the time they were created—the polar bear to the Arctic cold, the cod to salt water, and the woodpecker to hammering its beak into bark and so getting its food.

A freak woodpecker born with a soft beak could not survive, the creationists argued, because it would not be adapted to its environment. They carried this argument further by saying that any individual born with any unusual instinct or any unusual feature not held by the rest of the species would not survive. Any such changes in character, they maintained, must be changes for the worse. *Mutant* individuals, as such departures from mainstream types are called, which pop up commonly among all species, could not possibly be a change for the better, the creationists maintained. After all, God had created each species "perfect" to begin with. In this respect the creationists are quite right. Virtually all mutations do turn out to be disadvantageous, since the freak individuals are not in tune with the environment in some important way. But that is not to say that all mutations are disadvantageous.

It could not then and cannot now be denied that Earth changes. The geological evidence is overwhelming. During one period of time a certain place is gripped by cold. Much later, where there was once ice, tropical forests take root. Since the environment does change, then an animal species or a plant species that was "created" perfect in one moment of time, for one particular environment, would no longer be perfect centuries or thousands of years later when that environment had changed. To survive, the species would have to change to meet the changing conditions of the environment. And so species gradually evolve into new species in response to environmental change. In domestic breeding the process is hastened by man, so we can actually watch such changes taking place. But in nature the process is far too slow to observe directly.

With such reasoning, Darwin said that the creationists were wrong in thinking that all mutations are necessarily a change for the worse. Since the environment is always changing, then every now and then some changes, some departures from the species pattern among individual members of a species, must be changes for the better. There must be occasional changes that in some way enable the offspring to get on better than the parent during environmental change. Otherwise, unchanging species could not possibly survive amid environmental change.

A remarkably clear example of that idea took place in England in the mid-1800s, although the significance of it was not recognized until long after Darwin's time. A certain light-colored moth was common around the industrial city of Manchester during the mid-1800s. When these moths landed on the light-colored bark of trees in and around the city, their color blended so well with the color of the bark that moth-eating birds had trouble finding them. So the moth species was well protected from the bird predators.

From time to time, however, some of the offspring of the light-wing moths were born with dark wings instead of light wings. These dark-wing moths are the result of mutation, as is a kitten born with six toes on each paw or a turtle born with two heads. Some of these dark-wing moths lived long enough to produce dark-wing offspring, but not many managed to stay alive very long. When they landed on the light-bark trees, they showed up so well that the birds couldn't fail to see them. So the number of dark-wing moths was held down because these individuals were not well adapted to the environment. Here was an excellent example of what the creationists meant when they said that any change in the character of a new individual must be a change for the worse, since the species had been created "perfect" in the first place.

But then something interesting happened in Manchester. As more and more factories and houses were built, more coal was burned. More coal meant more soot in the air. Before long, the light-colored bark of the trees throughout Manchester and the surrounding area turned dark—not only from soot but from the death of light-colored lichens growing on the dull-colored bark. Pollution had changed the environment in a small but important way. It is not difficult to imagine what happened next: The light-wing moths were now at a disadvantage. They could easily be seen against the dark bark and were quickly eaten by the birds. But the few dark-wing moths were now protected. Their change in character (their dark color) was now working in their favor and they were being selected for. They were so well camouflaged against the dark bark that the birds overlooked them. Here was an excellent example of Darwin's principle of the survival of the fittest. Now it was the dark-wing variety that survived and reproduced more of its kind. The tables had turned.

There were countless examples of such struggles for survival in nature. Those individuals who were the most fit, who happened to have the right genetic makeup, survived amid environmental change. Those who lacked such favorable genetic makeup tended not to survive. That was how nature selected out certain individuals—the fittest ones—for survival. That is how natural selection works in the wild as well as in areas under man's control.

Darwin felt that there could be no mistake. Species change ever so gradually and evolve by natural selection. But how was he to convince others that this was so? It meant calling the Book of Genesis nothing more than a religious myth. To present his theory of evolution forcefully could be dangerous. Had it been 150 years or more earlier, he might have been burned at the stake for publishing such ideas of the Devil. In his own time, and this worried him very much, he risked exposing his family and close friends to harsh criticism and ridicule from those in positions of power who disagreed with him.

The time was 1856 and Darwin began to write out his views "pretty fully," not letting a single detail escape. His book was to be a huge technical volume, so well documented that he would include every imaginable argument that could be raised; and he would have airtight answers ready for each and every argument. His book was to be called *Natural Selection*. But then it happened.

On June 18, 1858, after Darwin had been writing for two years in the seclusion of Down House, his country home, he received a letter from a young naturalist named Alfred Russell Wallace who was doing research in the East Indies, as Darwin had aboard the *Beagle* some twenty years earlier. When Darwin read the letter, he was stunned. Almost word for word there was his own idea about how new species arise. If Darwin saw any merit in Wallace's ideas, would he please be good enough to forward the little essay on to Mr. Lyell? But, Wallace went on, if Darwin thought the idea absurd, then would he please destroy the essay. Immediately Darwin sent Lyell the copy of Wallace's essay, warmly praising it and sadly remarking that all his own work of these past long years "will be smashed."

Lyell and others knew well enough that Darwin had worked out his ideas on evolution long before Wallace had, and they were not about to see their good friend lose credit for it. At the same time, they could not ignore the fact that Wallace, quite independently, had arrived at the same idea. It turned out that both men were given credit for developing the theory of evolution through natural selection, and practically all textbooks today mention Wallace along with Darwin when evolution is discussed.

The Wallace episode convinced Darwin that he could not afford the luxury of taking many years to write his exhaustive *Natural Selection*. The shorter version he wrote was *The Origin of Species*. And immediately after it was published, the storm broke, as Darwin had expected. "Darwinism," as his and Wallace's theory came to be branded, was put on trial and attacked from the pulpit and in the classroom. Darwin was unjustly accused of saying that man descended from apes and monkeys. People making such attacks either failed to understand evolution, or they were deliberately twisting Darwin's ideas in order to discredit and ridicule him. Many fundamentalist religious groups to this day continue to do the same. For instance, in denouncing evolution, the Creation Research Society includes in one of their standard arguments the question: Who has ever seen an ape evolve into a man? Darwinism was "degrading to the human race," "grievously mischievous," "brazen lies," and Darwin was a "disgusting atheist," and so on and on came the ruthless attack. It was soon after this that Agassiz began his lecture series pointing out the dangers of Darwinism to the American people.

While there were critics galore, Darwin and evolution were not without their supporters. Many of the world's most influential scientists cheered evolution, seeing in it the most important single idea in all of biology, a unifying principle that brought all aspects of biology together.

The idea of evolution by natural selection appealed particularly to young scientists the world over. They were feeling restless with the old ideas of creationism, which they realized met a dead end with Adam and Eve. The idea of evolution opened up a new world to explore and to test and to build on. *The Origin of Species* was translated into many foreign languages immediately after it was published. Darwin was delighted to receive letters from German, Japanese, Scandinavian, and other scientists around the globe warmly praising him for his well-documented thesis.

Darwin had the art to present his argument for evolution on two levels, for he was fully aware that he would not win converts easily to this revolutionary idea on the basis of reason alone. People are not so made or so easily won over to a new point of view. The biologist Garrett Hardin reminds us of this:

> The patient scholar of Down House did not underrate the importance of esthetic arguments in moving the minds of men. *The Origin of Species* treats the demands of science as primary; but, those satisfied, Charles Darwin turned to esthetics to secure the internal consent of his readers to a new view of the past with which mankind can affiliate. The moving eloquence of the closing paragraph of this great work will bear repeating once more:
>
> *It is interesting to contemplate a tangled bank, clothed with many plants of many kinds, with birds singing on the bushes, with various insects flitting about, and with worms crawling through the damp earth, and to reflect that these elaborately constructed forms, so different from each other, and dependent upon each other in so complex a manner, have all been produced by laws acting around us. These laws, taken in the largest sense, being Growth with Reproduction; Inheritance which is almost implied by reproduction; Variability from the indirect and direct action of the conditions of life, and from use and*

disuse: a Ratio of Increase so high as to lead to a Struggle for Life, and as a consequence to Natural Selection, entitling Divergence of Character and the Extinction of less-improved forms. Thus, from the war of nature, from famine and death, the most exalted object which we are capable of conceiving, namely the production of the higher animals, directly follows. There is grandeur in this view of life, with its several powers, having been originally breathed by the Creator into a few forms or into one; and that, whilst this planet has gone cycling on according to the fixed law of gravity, from so simple a beginning endless forms most beautiful and most wonderful have been, and are being evolved.

This is not to say that the idea of evolution by natural selection was accepted by all scientists who studied the book. The vast majority of scientists today, however, regard evolution through natural selection not as a theory, but as fact.

Let me try to make crystal clear what is established beyond reasonable doubt, and what needs further study, about evolution. Evolution as a process that has always gone on in the history of the earth can be doubted only by those who are ignorant of the evidence or are resistant to evidence, owing to emotional blocks or to plain bigotry. By contrast, the mechanisms that bring evolution about certainly need study and clarification. There are no alternatives to evolution as history that can withstand critical examination. Yet we are constantly learning new and important facts about evolutionary mechanisms.
—Theodosius Dobzhansky (1973)

Still, there are many people who bitterly reject evolution purely on emotional grounds and strongly support the creationists' view. Some of these fundamentalist religious groups are so strong socially and politically and view evolution with such abhorrence that they often are successful in forcing textbook publishers to tone down their explanation of evolution or give "equal time" to the creationist view. The publishers frequently do so because they are afraid that their books will not enjoy wide sales in certain cities or states.

Judith V. Grabiner and Peter D. Miller recently completed a study in which they attempted to find out what effects the Scopes trial had on textbook publishers' treatment of evolution and Darwin. Perhaps some of you are familiar with that famous 1925 trial of John T. Scopes, who was found guilty of violating Tennessee's law against teaching the theory of evolution in public schools. "Events following the Scopes trial," according to Grabiner and Miller, "clearly show that the changes in the textbooks were responses to the antievolution movement and the fears it generated. . . . It is easy to identify a text published in the decade following 1925. Merely look up the word 'evolution' in the index or the glossary; you almost certainly will not find it. About its place in the text itself, it is harder to make generalizations." The two researchers might have applied that comment to the present decade as well.

As recently as 1973 one of the nation's largest and most influential publishers of textbooks issued a set of "guidelines" to the authors and consultants of its new science series. Among those guidelines was the following directive:

"Change the word 'evolution' to 'Biological Change' in student texts, grades 1–8, where it is a heading and/or where it appears in indexes and glossaries and throughout story-line of text."

Who are these creationists who are so powerful as a political force in the American schools and who wield such power over textbook publishers? As the magazine *Natural History* asks: "Will America become the laughingstock of the educated world by turning the clock back on Darwin's theory?" What are the creationists' views today, and how do the creationists justify those views?

7

❊❊❊

THE CREATIONISTS' STAND

❊❊❊

We do not know how God created, what processes He used, for God used processes which are not now operating anywhere in the natural universe. This is why we refer to divine creation as special creation. We cannot discover by scientific investigations anything about the creative processes used by God.

—Duane T. Gish (1973)

❊❊❊

The following is from a *New York Times* news story dated December 17, 1972:

> "Children are taught only one idea today—that the universe, life, and man are simply *accidents* that occurred by fortuitous chance without cause, purpose, or reason," said Dr. John R. Ford, a San Diego physician who is vice-president of the [California] board [of education]. While affirming the scientist's privilege to accept this "untestable hypothesis," he said, "I would at the same time propose that the same identical scientific data he uses to reach the conclusion will support equally well the hypothesis that these origins occurred by design with cause, purpose, and reason."

That, in broadest outline, is the heart of the creationists' argument against evolution and in support of the creation as described in the first chapter of Genesis. One of the chief spokesmen for the creationists is Dr. Duane T. Gish, associate director of the Institute for Creation Research and professor of natural science at the Christian Heritage College in San Diego, California. Dr. Gish is a biochemist who has done work at the Berkeley campus of the University of California and at the Medical College of Cornell University.

For those who are curious about the credentials of the Institute for Creation Research (also the Creation Research Society), according to Gish it is a "recently formed [1963] organization of Christian men of science, all of whom hold advanced degrees and are fully committed to the acceptance of Biblical and scientific creationism as opposed to evolution"; and further, that "science should be re-aligned within the framework of Biblical creationism."

CRS numbers in the neighborhood of 400 voting members plus about 1,200 sustaining and student members, mostly Protestant and strongly conservative in their theology. The creationists may well have a following of 20 million or more, if we take the nation's membership in evangelical churches as an index. CRS is an offshoot of a group known as the American Scientific Affiliation (ASA). In 1963 during an ASA meeting at Asbury College, Kentucky, one small group of members who found themselves in agreement about creationism and catastrophism formed the CRS splinter group because of ASA's failure to take a stand against evolution.

CRS's strong antievolution views are vigorously expounded in papers published by Gish, by Dr. Henry M. Morris, a Ph.D. in hydraulic engineering and director of CRS, and by various of its members. One of its publications, entitled *Evolution, the Fossils Say No!*, is prefaced with these words: "This book constitutes one of the most devastating critiques of evolution-

ary philosophy one could find. It goes right to the stronghold
of the supposed scientific evidence for evolution and demol-
ishes its central bastion."

❁❁❁❁❁

CREATIONISM,
EVOLUTION, AND FAITH

❁❁❁❁❁

Gish, whose name appears as author of the book, proceeds to explain why most scientists accept evolution. It has
"nothing to do, primarily, with the evidence," he writes. "The
reason that most scientists accept the theory of evolution is
that *most scientists are unbelievers, and unbelieving, materialistic men are forced to accept a materialistic, naturalistic explanation for the origin of all living things.*" In the same context
Gish also says, "The effects of prejudice and preconceived
ideas is of overwhelming importance in the acceptance of the
theory of evolution."

The ultraconservative views of CRS prevent acceptance
into its ranks of those who believe in God, accept the Bible
literally as "the word of God," but also believe in evolution,
saying that it is God's work from the level of molecules to that
of man. Or, as Gish likes to phrase it, "from fish to Gish."
Even a theistic form of evolution is totally unacceptable to
CRS since, according to Gish, "the first two chapters of Genesis were not written in the form of parables or poetry but
present the broad outlines of creation in the form of simple
historical facts, [and further that] these facts directly contradict evolution theory."

The creationists carefully structure their argument by saying "that the acceptance of creation requires an important
element of faith." They then add, "belief in evolution also

requires a vitally important element of faith," faith that the original cosmic egg of electrons, protons, and neutrons out of which the Universe presumably was created and subsequently evolved gave rise to the varied life about us today. "To believe *this*," writes Gish, "obviously requires a tremendous exercise of faith. Evolution theory is indeed no less religious nor more scientific than creation."

With evolution and creationism both established as "beliefs" based on faith, Gish then spends the remainder of the book comparing the two: "The question is, then, who has more evidence for his faith, the creationist or the evolutionist?" he asks.

❊❊❊

INTERPRETING
THE FOSSIL RECORD

❊❊❊

Evolutionists and creationists both agree on the fact well documented by Smith and Cuvier in the 1700s: that the various rock strata contain unique and characteristic assemblages of fossils. But that is about as far as agreement goes. It is the study of just such successive pages from the fossil record that the creationists base their argument on, because in their view, "the fossil record is much more in accord with the predictions based on creation rather than those based on the theory of evolution." In fact, they maintain, the fossil record strongly contradicts evolution theory.

According to evolution, first there were primitive single-cell forms, then multicell organisms, eventually the fishes, later amphibians, reptiles, birds, and mammals. If, for example, reptiles gave rise to birds, then there should be transitional fossil forms showing the gradual change, the creationists argue. For instance, if those great flying reptiles, the ptero-saurs, actually evolved from a nonflying reptile, Gish says, then transitional forms showing gradual change in the length of the fourth finger along with other changes should appear in the fossil record. Where are the transitional forms linking fishes with the amphibians? the creationists ask. Where are the fossils of those individuals that show a transition of fins into feet and legs? "It seems clear," Gish concludes, "that after 150 years of intense searching, a large number of obvi-ous transitional forms [occurring throughout the fossil record] would have been discovered if the predictions of evolution theory are valid. . . . The discovery of only five or six of the transitional forms scattered through time would be sufficient to document evolution."

If the evolution model is correct, the creationists maintain, then the older rock strata that are supposed to contain the earlier forms of life should be followed by hundreds and thou-sands of transitional forms linking subsequent major groups of organisms. New major groups should *not* appear suddenly in the fossil record, they argue; but indeed they do, the creation-ists correctly point out.

If the creation model is correct, then the fossil record should be consistent with what the Bible says: that is, during the days of creation as described in the first chapter of Genesis all of the "basic kinds" of plants and animals were created and no more would have been created since that time. Genesis 2:2 mentions a "finished" creation. Although new varieties have occurred, not a single new basic kind (species) has, say the creationists. Different breeds of dogs and cats are "varieties," while all dogs and all cats are two distinct species, or basic kinds. The creation model, then, would predict the sudden appearance of basic kinds of plants and animals with absolutely no evidence of fossil ancestors. Further, there should be no fossil evidence of any common ancestors of men, apes and monkeys, for example. Any evolutionist will readily agree that the fossil record is frustratingly incomplete. For instance, what evolution recognizes as man's earliest known ancestors (the chordates) appear suddenly during the Ordovician period with no traces of evolutionary links with the past.

If the creationists accepted radioactive dating as a reliable method of determining the age of rocks, and therefore of the fossils those rocks contain, their argument would be considerably weakened. But they do not accept radioactive dating, at least CRS doesn't. In his fossils book, Gish says that there is no direct way of determining the age of any rock. While he admits that the presently used methods of determining the ratios of uranium to lead or potassium to argon in a given rock sample are accurate, he says that these methods cannot be used to tell how old rocks are. The reason is that we have no way of knowing what the original ratio was when the rocks were formed. (Geologists do not agree.) Without knowing that, even the most accurate measurements of the ratio today can tell us nothing about the age of a rock, says Gish. The significance of this, of course, is that there is no direct evidence for Earth being billions or even millions of years old. Instead, Earth can be a young planet and the biblical 6 days of creation occurring about 6,000 years ago can be taken as literally true.

Those creationists who do accept radioactive dating of rock as reliable have suggested that the six days of biblical creation were not twenty-four-hour days, but "days" spanning many millions of years, each in accordance with the geologic time chart. CRS refuses to give an inch on this intramural issue. Gish underlines the conservative view by adding, "Furthermore, the genealogies listed in Genesis and elsewhere in the Bible, it is believed, would restrict the time of creation to

somewhere between six thousand and about ten thousand
years ago."

❧❧❧

CATASTROPHISM
REVIVED

❧❧❧

It was James Hutton in the 1700s who first said that
the forces that mold and change Earth's surface today are the
same ones that have always operated and that they have been
operating over periods of millions of years with "no vestige of
a past, and no prospect of an end." This concept of uniformitarianism, as it came to be called, maintained, "the present is
the key to the past." The doctrine was challenged vigorously
by Baron Cuvier, a creationist who advocated the principle of
catastrophism: world-shaking catastrophes such as the Noachian flood periodically wiped out entire species. God then
created new assemblages of species, evidence for which is
found in the sudden appearance of new species in the fossil
record.

Although catastrophism was dealt a death blow by Charles
Lyell in the 1830s and has never since regained geological
respect, CRS members fully subscribe to it. The Noachian
flood, they maintain, was only one of many catastrophes
wrought by God. Further, it was not just a local event but
worldwide in scope.

The creationists argue that uniformitarianism is far too slow
a process of geological change to account for the abrupt geological formations found in the rock record. It is impossible,
they maintain, to account for most of the world's "important
geological formations" according to uniformitarian principles.
Among such formations they include the Tibetan Plateau,
some 750,000 square miles of sedimentary deposits measuring

thousands of feet in thickness; the Karoo formation of Africa, supposedly containing 800 billion vertebrate animal fossils; the herring fossil bed in the Miocene shales of California; and others. The creationists look to the suddenness of the Noachian flood as responsible for such geological formations. They add that accompanying such a devastating event there would be "attendant vast earth movements, volcanic action, dramatic changes in climate conditions, and other catastrophic events. The fossil record, rather than being a record of transformation, is a record of mass destruction, death, and burial by water and its contained sediments."

.Although "a massive reexamination and reinterpretation of geologic data is required" to justify catastrophism, they argue, the situation was prophesied by the Apostle Peter in the Second Epistle 3:3–6. Creationist geologists presumably are now at work reinterpreting the geologic data according to "flood geology," which necessarily includes as well a reevaluation of all radioactive dating methods. Among the Institute for Creation Research's many projects is "an ongoing search for Noah's ark on Mount Ararat." According to Henry Morris, in charge of CRS' Ararat Project, "Popular concepts of origins would be greatly altered by the rediscovery of the Ark of Noah. Any model of earth history which uses as its basic assumption the doctrine of uniformitarianism would be found inadequate."

🌼🌼

WHAT IS A SPECIES?

🌼🌼

If you read any of the CRS literature, you will come across references to "basic kinds" of animals. Sometimes a

basic kind seems to be a given species, but other times the
creationist may use "basic kind" to refer to what traditional
biology regards as two or more different species. Gish provides
an example by saying that all humans are within the single
basic kind, *Homo sapiens*. But he next says that a creationist
may use basic kind in a much larger context. Instead of being
restricted to the species level, basic kind can conveniently be
used one level higher, on the genus level. For example, Gish
says that because the various species of coyote are so similar,
they can be regarded as one basic kind and, in all likelihood,
right along with wolves and dogs. He further says that Darwin's various species of Galápagos finches probably should
be grouped as one basic kind, as should the various species of
sweet corn, popcorn, dent corn, starch corn, and flint corn. So
the creationist does not always accept the traditional species
catagories, preferring instead to broaden some of them into
more inclusive groups such as "dog kind," "corn kind," and
so on.

The creationists readily admit that variations occur within
their basic-kinds categories of animals, such as collies, terriers,
great Danes, scotties, and presumably wolves and coyotes,
among the dog kind. Some variation, they say, was planned
by God to enhance the survival of a basic kind, "making it
more readily possible for them to survive in the various environmental situations to which they are exposed." Other
variations "are simply an expression of the Creator's desire to
show as much beauty of flower, variety of song in birds, or
interesting types of behavior in animals as possible." Both of
these observations about variation are made in the Creation
Research Society's high school biology textbook entitled *Biology: A Search for Order in Complexity*.

Nearly all biologists take a somewhat narrower and less
flexible view of species than CRS does, which is not to imply

that all biologists agree to a neat and tidy definition of what constitutes a species. Fortunately, however, there happens to be more agreement than disagreement. In the late 1930s Dobzhansky defined species as "groups of actually or potentially interbreeding natural populations, which are reproductively isolated from other such groups." More recently the zoologist Ernst Mayr has defined species simply as organisms that do or can interbreed. According to the biologist George Gaylord Simpson, "species are populations of [interbreeding] individuals of common descent, living together in similar ecological relationships and tending to have a unified and continuing evolutionary role distinct from that of other species."

From the creationists' point of view there is, of course, an extremely important advantage to keeping one's species loose. If, for example, all of Darwin's finches are lumped together as a single species, there is no need to suppose that all evolved independently from a common ancestral type, as evolution maintains. The creationists say that indeed there was an ancestral type, a master blueprint, but when God created the master type He created the "variations" right along with it. The CRS textbook resolves the species problem of Darwin's finches this way:

> We find in this brief mention of Darwin's finches a highly variable species that very likely populated the islands originally as a flock of finches. Their chance settlement of the various islands set up a distribution such that only *Geospiza scandens* thrives on certain islands, *G. magnirostris* on the other islands, and other "genera" in similar random distribution. The basic song pattern is reported to be the same with slight variation in the various genera. To date attempts to hybridize different groups of finches have been unsuccessful, but animals often fail to reproduce in captivity. The degree of intergradation is remarkable and were it not for the historical value, with regard

to Darwin's life, placed on these birds it is doubtful if they would still be retained as true species.

So each basic kind of plant and animal, according to the creationists, was created according to a master plan, although with minor variations for survival value and to break the monotony. Gish reminds us:

> The variation that has occurred since the end of the creative work of God has been limited to changes within kinds . . . and each kind was created with sufficient genetic potential, or gene pool, to give rise to all of the varieties within that kind that have existed in the past and those that are yet in existence today. . . . No matter what combinations [of genes] may occur, however, the human kind always remains human, and the dog kind never ceases to be dog. The transformations proposed by the theory of evolution never take place.

❊❊❊

FROM VARIATION
TO SIMILARITY

❊❊❊

If God went to the trouble to create variations on a master plan for basic kinds of plants and animals, then why did He go to the further trouble of creating so many similarities among different basic kinds? This is what the evolutionists ask. The study of living organisms and the fossils of extinct organisms shows many remarkable similarities in body plan and function. Such similarities among such major groups as humans, birds, and horses are said to be *homologous*. Evolutionists reason that such homologous structures and functions are evidence that two such groups are related. The creationists, on the other hand, maintain that this is only an unfounded assumption and in no way is "evidence" that two such groups are related genetically.

For example, the illustrations on page 164 show the fore-limbs of a lizard, salamander, bird, whale, mole, horse, dog, and human. All of these animals are classified as primates. Biologists now think that the first primate animals were small shrewlike animals that lived about 60 million years ago. All the other primates, according to evolution, developed from those shrewlike animals, which would explain why the hands of all primates are so very much alike.

The creationists take a different view of the situation. In the case of the forelimbs all are used for moving about, although each is specialized for certain environmental conditions. The creationists argue that when God created the vertebrates, for example, "He used a single blueprint," as the CRS biology textbook points out, "for the body plan but varied the plan so that each 'kind' would be perfectly equipped to take its place in the wonderful world He created for them."

❊❊❊

BATTLE
OF THE BONES

❊❊❊

It is difficult to pinpoint the time when the creation *versus* evolution controversy began in this country. As good a date as any is when Agassiz inaugurated his Boston lectures on the heels of the publication of *The Origin of Species* in 1859. Over the years the controversy has reemerged on the state level here and there. The most memorable occasion, of course, was the famous "Monkey Trial" of John T. Scopes in Dayton, Tennessee, in 1925.

A young biology teacher of twenty-four at the time, Scopes

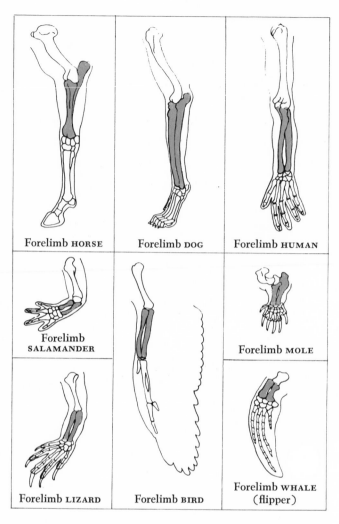

Forelimb HORSE   Forelimb DOG   Forelimb HUMAN

Forelimb SALAMANDER   Forelimb MOLE

Forelimb LIZARD   Forelimb BIRD   Forelimb WHALE (flipper)

✺ *"The conclusion is inescapable that the limb bones of man, the bat, and the whale are modifications of a common ancestral pattern. The facts admit of no other logical interpretation . . . the forelimbs of all tetrapod vertebrates exhibit a unity of anatomical pattern intelligible only on the basis of common inheritance."—Peter E. Volpe,* Understanding Evolution, *William C. Brown Company, Publishers.*

✺ *"We might assume that in shaping forelimbs the Creator used a certain pattern; when he created the hand of man He modified that pattern in a certain way; when He created the wing of a bat He modified the pattern in a different way; when he created legs adapted for rapid running He modified the pattern in still a different way; and so on. According to this theory there is no genetic relationship between man, bat, and horse; all they have in common is that they were made by the same creator."—Paul A. Moody,* Introduction to Evolution, *Harper &Row, Publishers, Inc.* SCIENCE PHOTO/GRAPHICS, LTD.

had violated a new state law that prohibited the teaching of human evolution. He submitted to a fake "arrest," and after a ten-day trial that was followed around the world he was found guilty and gained instant fame. The Tennessee Supreme Court later nullified Scope's conviction, terming the entire episode "bizarre." Days later he was plagued with movie contracts, lecture engagements, and a variety of commercial offers, all of which he declined. He settled later in the year for a three-year stint of graduate study in geology at the University of Chicago, paid for from a fund raised by the many scientists and reporters who had come to know him.

In 1965 an Arkansas biology teacher named Susan Epperson violated that state's antievolution law and subsequently carried her case all the way to the Supreme Court in 1968 and won. In 1972 the last antievolution law in the United States—in Mississippi—was removed from the books. Legislators simply omitted the old law from a new state code. Even while that tactful move was being made, antievolution sentiments were smoldering and being rekindled in a number of states, among them Texas and California.

As early as 1970, Texas's State Textbook Commission had refused to authorize the purchase of several newly published biology textbooks because they treated evolution in such an outspoken way. Wrote the Commission: "In the category of life science, grade 7, each book shall carry a statement on an introductory page that any material on evolution included in the book is presented as a theory rather than as a fact."

In 1971, the Board of Education of Columbus, Ohio, passed a resolution encouraging teachers to teach special creation right along with evolution through natural selection whenever the origin of life was discussed. In the following year, after nine long years, California's State Board of Education ruled that all science textbooks must present evolution not as a fact but only as a theory. What the creationists had wanted originally, but didn't manage to get, was something much stronger —equal time with evolution for the teaching of special creation as a tenable scientific theory in the science classroom.

Since the time of the 1972 ruling in California, the State Board of Education has taken an additional step to meet the demands of the creationists by further ruling that in all social science textbooks that present evolution, equal recognition of special creation also be given. Meanwhile, the creationists continue to be a strong force in convincing science textbook publishers to include creationism along with evolution. At the time this is being written, more than fifteen states have introduced legislation specifying that in public schools equal time is to be provided for points of view other than evolution when the origin and development of life—essentially meaning man—are dealt with.

Typical of such legislation was a 1973 Tennesee law, which as a bill was approved by both the House and Senate by votes of twenty-eight to one and fifty-four to fifteen respectively. The law replaced Tennessee's old antievolution law, which remained on the books until 1967. The new law read:

Any biology textbook used for teaching in the public schools which expresses an opinion of, or relates to, a theory about origins or creation of man and his world shall be prohibited from being used as a textbook in such system unless it specifically states that it is a theory as to the origin and creation of man and his world and is not represented to be scientific fact. Any textbook so used in the public education system which expresses an opinion or relates to a theory or theories shall give in the same textbook and under the same subject commensurate attention to, and an equal amount of emphasis on, the origins and creation of man and his world as the same is recorded in other theories, including, but not limited to, the Genesis account in the Bible.

The bill was passed by the Senate without a murmur of debate. The reason, according to its sponsor, Senator Milton Hamilton, "is that the national TV came down here with the idea they would make us look like a bunch of nitpickers. You know, like barefoot Tennesseans." One of the individuals instrumental in encouraging the bill's passage is the biologist and CRS member, Russell C. Artist. Listed as an author of the CRS biology textbook, Artist tried to convince the Tennessee State Textbook Commission to adopt the text for statewide use, but so far it has not done so.

The ambivalence with which lawmakers regard the evolution-creation controversy was again demonstrated on April 10, 1975, when the U.S. Court of Appeals for the Sixth Circuit struck down as unconstitutional Tennessee's 1973 "equal time" law. According to the editors of *Science* magazine, "The importance of the ruling transcends the boundaries of Tennessee. It possibly marks the end to a nationwide campaign by fundamentalists to adulterate the teaching of evolution." *Science* may be unduly optimistic; in any event, in making the ruling Circuit Judge George Edwards said that, "For such a state to seek to enforce such a preference [for Genesis over evolution] by law is to seek to accomplish the very establishment of religion, which the First Amendment to the Constitution of the United States squarely forbids."

Although nearly all scientists regard the Creation Research Society's stand as bizarre, there can be no doubt that the creationists, whenever they are successful, are meeting a real need felt by many people. Their recent growth in popularity is evidence enough. In November 1972 a comprehensive statement prepared by Gish was given before the California State Board of Education. It is presented in its entirety here:

While religious implications are obvious, the issue of creation
versus evolution is not a question of religion *versus* science.
No one is attempting to introduce the Bible into the classroom.
At issue is the cause of academic freedom—the right of the
teachers in our schools to teach competing theories concerning
origins and the right of the students to be apprised of all the
evidence in relation to these theories. We have on one hand
the theory of evolution, devoid of direction, design, or goal,
and on the other hand origins by special creation through
design, purpose, and specific goals of a Creator.

Creation has not been witnessed by human observers; it is not
repeatable; it cannot be demonstrated experimentally, and as
a theory it is non-falsifiable. The general theory of evolution
(molecules-to-man theory) also fails to meet these three criteria.
As all honest scientists must admit, evolution has not been witnessed by human observers (who has seen a fish evolve into an
amphibian or an ape into man?). It is obviously not repeatable.
In addition, as the well-known evolutionist and geneticist, Richard B. Goldschmidt, has stated, transformation, even at the
species level, cannot be demonstrated experimentally. The
changes that are actually observable in nature or testable in
the laboratory are of a trivial nature in relation to the grand
scheme of particles-to-people evolution. Finally, as an increasing
number of evolutionists are complaining, modern evolution
theory is so plastic it is non-falsifiable. It can be used to explain
anything and everything.

Furthermore, to believe that we humans and all other forms
of life are the products of a ball of electrons, protons, and neutrons which exploded billions of years ago, and that our origin
was due solely to properties inherent in these sub-atomic particles, obviously requires a tremendous exercise in faith.

In the light of the above considerations, it is clear that special
creation is neither more religious nor less scientific than evolution. Each is a postulate which may serve as a model to correlate
and explain the evidence related to origins and to make pre-

dictions concerning the nature of natural phenomena and future discoveries.

Special creation not only offers a credible explanation of the evidence related to origins, but thousands of scientists believe that it offers a much more credible explanation than evolution. For example, the design, purpose, and complexity of a watch gives obvious evidence that it had a creator. A living cell is infinitely more complex that a watch, and every detail of its structure and function gives evidence of design and purposefulness. Does this not then give evidence that it, too, had a Creator?

Two of the laws of biology are that life comes only from pre-existing life, and that like always begets like. Such empirical scientific evidence is in accord with the creation model, but evolutionists must postulate untestable hypotheses to render such evidence compatible with evolution theory.

Mutations are disordering processes in highly ordered structures which lower the viability of the affected organisms. Natural selection is a conservative process that eliminates the unfit produced by mutations and other deleterious processes. Thousands of scientists disagree with the evolutionary postulate that the combination of a deleterious process and a conserving mechanism could have produced a vast array of highly complex and marvelously designed living organisms from a single primeval cell.

A group of mathematicians, who themselves ascribe to evolutionary philosophy, came to the conclusion that, based on probability considerations, the modern theory of evolution is totally inadequate to explain more than trivial change. Dr. Murray Eden, one of these mathematicians, and a professor at Massachusetts Institute of Technology, stated that, " . . . an adequate scientific theory of evolution must await the discovery and elucidation of new natural laws—physical, physico-chemical, and biological." How could anyone then, in good conscience, demand that modern evolution theory be taught as dogma, as the only explanation for the origin of the universe and of all living things?

The fossil record gives evidence that life appeared suddenly (on a geologic time-scale) on this planet in great diversity and at a high level of complexity, without evidence of evolutionary ancestors. The fossil record then reveals a remarkable absence of the many transitional forms predicted on the basis of evolution theory. As leading paleontologists have acknowledged, gaps are regular and systematic between higher categories of plants and animals. For example, there are absolutely no traces of intermediate stages between the major types of invertebrates or between invertebrates and vertebrates. Furthermore, nowhere can be found a part-fish, part-amphibian showing, for instance, half-fins, half-feet. Flight supposedly evolved four times independently—in birds, insects, reptiles, and mammals (bats). In not one of these four cases can an intermediate be found between the flying animal possessing full power of flight and its supposed non-flying ancestor. Yet, if evolution is true, our museums should be full of easily-recognizable intermediates. Such evidence fits admirably the predictions of the creation model but contradicts the predictions of the evolution model.

Under our present situation, students are being brain-washed in evolution philosophy. They are given all of the evidence that can be adduced in favor of the theory with no exposure to its fallacies and weaknesses. No attempt is made to demonstrate the manner in which scientific evidence can be so eminently correlated and explained by the concept of special creation.

The majority in the scientific community and educational circles are using the cloak of "science" to force the teaching of their particular world view upon our students and the public in general. The dogma of rationalistic materialism is smothering full and free inquiry in science and violating the constitutional guarantee against a state-supported religion or philosophic system. It is time for a change.

8

㸽㹌㹌㸽

THE
EVOLUTIONISTS'
STAND

㸽㹌㹌㸽

*Does the evolutionary doctrine clash with
religious faith? It does not. It is a blunder to
mistake the Holy Scriptures for elementary
textbooks of astronomy, geology, biology, and
anthropology. Only if symbols are construed
to mean what they are not intended to mean
can there arise imaginary, insoluble conflicts.*
—Theodosius Dobzhansky (1973)

㸽㹌㹌㸽

THE SCIENTIFIC
COMMUNITY RESPONDS

㸽㹌㹌㸽

The following statement is from the Bulletin of the
American Association for the Advancement of Science, dated
February 1973:

The Commission of Science Education, of the American Association for the Advancement of Science, is vigorously opposed
to attempts by some boards of education, and other groups, to

require that religious accounts of creation be taught in science classes.

During the past century and a half, the Earth's crust and the fossils preserved in it have been intensively studied by geologists and paleontologists. Biologists have intensively studied the origin, structure, physiology, and genetics of living organisms. The conclusion of these studies is that the living species of animals and plants have evolved from different species that lived in the past. The scientists involved in these studies have built up the body of knowledge known as the biological theory of the origin and evolution of life. There is no currently acceptable alternative scientific theory to explain the phenomena.

The various accounts of creation that are part of the religious heritage of many people are not scientific statements or theories. They are statements that one may choose to believe, but if he does, this is a matter of faith, because such statements are not subject to study or verification by the procedures of science. A scientific statement must be capable of tests by observation and experiment. It is acceptable only if, after repeated testing, it is found to account satisfactorily for the phenomena to which it is applied.

Thus the statements about creation that are part of many religions have no place in the domain of science, and should not be regarded as reasonable alternatives to scientific explanations for the origin and evolution of life.

The geobiologist Norman D. Newell echoed the AAAS stand when he wrote in *Natural History* magazine:

Professional biologists in various parts of the United States have protested the lobbying tactics of the creationists, and several of the nation's academic and scientific organizations have passed resolutions condemning the creationists' proposals on the grounds that special creation is theology, not science, and should not be represented to public school children as a reasonable scientific alternative to the theory of organic evolution.

In 1972, when California's State Board of Education made its ruling about presenting creationism as a viable alternative to evolution, nineteen Nobel laureates signed a letter of protest. They maintained, "no alternative to the evolutionary theory gives an equally satisfactory explanation of the biological fact." The National Academy of Science added its voice of condemnation by issuing the following statement:

> The result of including creationism in otherwise nonreligious textbooks would be to impair the proper segregation of the teaching and understanding of science and religion. The foundations of science must exclude appeal to supernatural causes not susceptible to validation by objective criteria. Science and religion being mutually exclusive realms of human thought, their presentation in the same context is likely to lead to misunderstanding of both scientific theory and religious belief.

One of the most devastating blows to the creationists' argument was delivered by Richard P. Aulie, a historian of biology and medicine. In two long articles appearing in the April and May issues (1972) of *The American Biology Teacher*, he takes a hard look at the creationists' most comprehensive document to date, their high school biology textbook, *Biology: A Search for Order in Complexity*, prepared by the textbook committee of the Creation Research Society in 1970.

🌼🌼🌼

DESIGN

🌼🌼🌼

Aulie organizes his attack on CRS under three headings: design, catastrophism, and the ideal type, or the creationists' version of "species," which they call "basic kind." He points out that in at least nine passages in the CRS text the authors give examples of God the Creator designing *purpose* into nature, an idea that virtually all biologists reject. One example of this "teleological" view, as it is called, is the passage of the CRS text stating that variation in plants and animals "is simply an expression of the Creator's desire to show as much beauty of flower, variety of song in birds, or interesting types of behavior in animals as possible." Comments Newell, "presumably for the delectation of human beings."

Similarities in anatomical structure between species is also cited by CRS as evidence of design on the part of the Creator. (Examples of such similarity in the structure of the forelimbs of humans, dogs, horses, and other vertebrates were shown on page 164.) "The Creator *chose* to use a common pattern," CRS points out, when He created each species independently. More than a century earlier aboard the *Beagle* Captain Fitz-Roy had patiently explained to Darwin that structural similarities between species were designed by God, and our cleverness in detecting those similarities reveals to us scientific proof of God's wisdom. Newell reminds us, "organic evolutionists attribute variations to genetic recombinations and mutations. Similarities in form, structure, and DNA proteins are believed to be indications of a common origin and the descent of one species from another."

Aulie points out:

> We do not observe design in nature. Rather, our minds seem to be so constructed that we can perceive regularities to which, if we have religious presuppositions, we apply the concept of design. Furthermore, to make of design a biologic principle, as in these passages in the CRS book, is to reduce the need to interpret biologic processes as precursors of the adaptation that evokes wonder. Modern biology is then in jeopardy. The CRS

position must lead inevitably to the view (although the authors do not go this far) that biologic processes cannot expresss cause-and-effect relationships; that is, they must be merely a series of discrete and unrelated events. If design is a sufficient and exclusive explanation of how an amoeba moves, then it is all right to study its environmental conditions; but we can never be sure that they are causal agencies that influence such behavior.

According to Aulie, the creationists regard natural selection as posing a threat to theism, but they do not similarly regard a purely physical agency such as gravity, although they should. "After all," he asks, "if gravity holds the planets in orbit, then the Almighty is not on the job. Why not simply say that Mars was 'designed' to travel in an elliptical orbit and so dispense with gravity entirely?"

❦❦❦

CATASTROPHISM

❦❦❦

The creationists' choice of catastrophism over uniform-itarianism is a strictly nineteenth-century belief that modern geologists no longer entertain, Aulie writes. As in the 1800s, the creationists today continue to be firmly convinced that the Noachian flood can be supported by the geological record. They also continue to support the notion of special creation following each world-shaking catastrophe, as described by Cuvier. According to Aulie, again referring to the CRS biology text:

Groups of organisms succeed one another in the rocks, there are no transition fossils, and discontinuities indicate that major changes occurred in the past by geologic agencies no longer in operation. Noah's flood was the most important and recent of these agencies. Moreover, we are invited to believe that Noah's flood scoured out the Grand Canyon and deposited the fossils in the wake of this swift, paroxysmal convulsion, which engulfed the whole earth.

Thus special creation is to the CRS authors a scientific doctrine; it is more persuasive that the alternative view [of evolution]. Undaunted by more than a century of scholarship in geology and paleontology and a half-century in genetics, they argue that no evolutionary change has occurred in time—for the major groups of organisms were created fully formed, *ex nihilo*, at the beginning. In short: the chicken came before the egg.

In another instance Aulie asks:

If Noah's flood scoured out the Grand Canyon, would CRS be able to find for us marks of this flood on say, the upper slopes of Mt. Whitney, or perhaps on Mt. Hood? After all, "the mountains were covered" (Genesis 7:20). But Lyell did not find that such a single devastation could account for the present or past characteristics of the Mississippi Valley, which he visited in 1845–46. If he was correct, how then could the flood account for the Grand Canyon—much less any change at higher elevation?

Aulie relates a visit he made in 1954 to the site of Ur of the Chaldees, the ancestral home of Abraham. Standing in a large pit partly filled with desert sand, he recalled accounts of the famed British archeologist Sir Leonard Woolley standing in the same place some thirty years earlier. Woolley had found a layer of sediments about an inch thick, evidence of a large-scale local disaster dated about 3200 B.C. Woolley concluded: "There could be no doubt that the flood of which we had thus found the only possible evidence was the Flood of Sumerian history and legend, the Flood on which was based the story of Noah." Seemingly vast in extent, the flood certainly covered "all the high hills" around, which for the people living there at the time represented "the face of the whole earth" (Genesis 7:19, 8:9). The point Woolley is making is that indeed there is evidence for a major flood in Sumerian times, and it was that flood that became the basis for the Gilgamesh legend, which later on was recast as the present biblical version of Noah's flood.

The geological record clearly confirms creation week, as described in Genesis, according to the CRS text. Among the "evidence" cited in the text in support of man being created only hours later than plants and marine organisms is a fossil of a "human-like sandal print with several trilobites in it [found near Delta, Utah, in 1968]. From this, one can deduce that man and trilobites lived at the same time. . . . Another spectacular find was that of giant men's footprints in a Cretaceous river bed near Glen Rose, Texas. Also found in the same bed were dinosaur and brontosaurus tracks. Clearly this makes possible the deduction that man and the dinosaur lived at the same time."

The following item, under the headline "Textbook on Creation Rejected as Inaccurate," appeared in *The New York Times* datelined Atlanta, June 22, 1974, UP:

> A textbook that teaches the divine theory of creation has been turned down by the Atlanta School Board on the grounds that it is biased and inaccurate.
>
> The book, *Biology: A Search for Order in Complexity*, had been approved by the State Board of Education after some legislators threatened to force state high schools to teach divine creation in biology classes.
>
> The Atlanta board approved Monday a report that said the

✽ In 1731, the fossil shown here was identified as the remains of a human who had been drowned in the Noachian flood, and so was called Homo diluvii testis. The fossil turned out to be that of a salamander.

book "contains numerous errors in terms of established biological fact."

It said the purpose of the book was to present both sides of the theory of divine creation and evolution, but that it presented only one side, divine creation.

A member of the textbook committee, Katherine Hertzka, said, "We have no quarrel with different theories when they are properly presented. But this text was just poorly written and out of date."

꧁꧁꧁꧁꧁꧁꧁꧁꧁꧁꧁꧁꧁꧁꧁꧁꧁꧁꧁꧁꧁꧁꧁꧁꧁꧁꧁꧁꧁

The alleged footprints of large humans are supposed to substantiate the Genesis 6:4 account of "giants in the earth," according to Aulie. He goes on to say:

Keith Young, professor of geology at the University of Texas at Austin, has informed me . . . that on several visits to the Glen Rose, Texas, location he has never seen, nor has he been shown, such "human" footprints, though there are dinosaur tracks to be seen there. Moreover, he observes that the published pictures of "human" tracks show no pressure points as the result of walking, whereas the dinosaur tracks do show the flow of mud as the animal shifted its footing when walking; there is no narrowing of the "human" instep; and the "human" tracks are chiselled evenly, whereas the dinosaur tracks, made in soft mud, show deformation due to the rolling-in of the mud.

As for the "human-like sandal print" at Delta, Utah, R. A. Robinson, professor of geology at the University of Utah, has informed me . . . that the supposed "footprint" has probably resulted from a fracture pattern that commonly occurs in certain sedimentary layers there. Moreover, the "footprint" occurs in company with trilobites, brachiopods, and echinoderms—creatures of the ocean, which is a strange habitat indeed for antediluvian man.

In concluding the first part of his review of the CRS text, Aulie writes:

> Catastrophism sought to maintain a short time span for the earth by accounting for observable changes in terms of sudden convulsions. Lyell lengthened the age of the earth by arguing effectively for gradual, long-term changes. Those persons who today are drawn to the former view ought to weigh the arguments put forward in Lyell's *Principles of Geology*. It is Lyell, not Darwin, whose monumental achievement remains a challenge to the reestablishment of this 19th-century doctrine by the Creation Research Society.

❧❧❧

IDEAL TYPE

❧❧❧

The creationists readily admit that there are many similarities in structure, form, and physiology from species to species. They also admit that within a given species, such as the common house cat, there is variability of breed. Aulie tells us that since the time of Aristotle biologists have been trying to account for variation and homologues. Darwin's solution was common ancestry with hereditary relatedness. CRS maintains that similarity and variation both were God's work at the time of the creation: "Creationists believe that when God created the vertebrates, He used a single blueprint for the body plan but varied the plan so that each 'kind' would be perfectly equipped to take its place in the wonderful world He created for them."

The "blueprint" the CRS text refers to dates back to the Greek philosopher Plato and became a major concern of the nineteenth-century creationist Richard Owen. It was Owen who coined the term "homologues" to describe such biological similarities among species. He came to the conclusion, Aulie relates, "that vertebrate skeletons are modifications of a single 'archetype' that existed as a divine reality, wholly apart and beyond nature." In other words, each breed of cat or dog or rose is but one version of an ideal type, which the creationists call a "basic kind." It does not exist in reality but only as a blueprint in God's mind. "Similar animals are therefore varying manifestations of a single idea (*eidos*) that has an existence of its own, quite beyond the realm of the verifiable," writes Aulie.

The CRS text says that a single blueprint was sufficient for all seven classes of vertebrates—three classes of fishes, one of amphibians, one of reptiles, one of birds, and one of mammals. But when they come to the mollusks, they say that each of the five classes was created according to the plan of a different blueprint. Each blueprint of each basic kind, according to the creationists, is timeless and never changes. Biological variations must, therefore, be slight departures from an unchanging ideal type of which the Creator was architect. Darwin was the first to cite variation as evidence that species are not constant, but that they change. Until he published *The Origin of Species* biologists had no alternative to the creationists' basic-kind idea. Although Darwin recognized the significance of variations in evolution, he did not know what caused them or how variation was passed on by one generation to the next. Today we know the causes—mutations and the genetic recombinations made possible by sexual reproduction.

Darwin's finches of the Galápagos serve as a good example of how the creationists use the Platonic ideal type instead of the modern view of species to justify Genesis on scientific grounds. They cite a recent study of 1,200 Galápagos finches at the California Academy of Sciences museum in San Francisco. "All assigned species intergrade with one another," the CRS text says. The authors further claim as convincing evidence that all the Galápagos finches actually belong to one species the fact that "a perfect gradation would be found between the species having the largest beak . . . and the species having the smallest beak" when all are arranged according to body and beak size. Says Aulie, "Apparently, if Darwin had only recognized this gradation he would not have been led astray. But when we consult his *Voyage of the Beagle* . . . we find that it is precisely this gradation that caught his attention." It was also what led him to recognize the ways of natural selection.

Aulie concludes his criticism of the creationists' basic kind by saying, "to affirm that all things were created by God is not the same as saying that the Creator employed a blueprint for the creation. The former assertion is derived from the Judaeo-Christian tradition; the latter is merely an extension of Greek doctrine." Aulie asks earlier, "What texts in the Bible would CRS put forward as documentation for 'patterns,' 'systems,' and 'blueprints'?" He answers, "Of course, there are none. (Only John 1:1–3 and 2 Corinthians 4:18 are suggestive, but in context the meaning of each is entirely different.)"

✻✻✻

CAN CREATIONISM
UNDERMINE BIOLOGY?

✻✻✻

Aulie is neither alarmed nor deeply disturbed over the creationists' return. One reason is that Lyell in his *Principles of Geology* once and for all time

replaced violence [catastrophism] with tranquillity [uniformitarianism] and extended the age of the earth. . . . This achievement alone is one of two reasons why I find it inconceivable that the CRS text authors, however brave their effort, can now bring about any major redirection of biology teaching to the conceptual framework of this period before Darwin. . . . I can think of no instance where a new doctrine, once embraced, was rejected for a return to that of a previous age. This is the second reason why I cannot see how the CRS text authors, however sincere they may be, can expect much success in their efforts to return biology to the early part of the 19th century. Science, like time, is a forward movement.

Garrett Hardin shows more concern:

Each new generation brings a fresh attack on the doctrine of evolution. Eternal vigilance is called for by biologists. Facts must be displayed once more; arguments must be explained. But this is not enough. The *beauty* of the evolutionary viewpoint must be made evident. It is not enough for teaching biologists to be good scientists in the narrow sense. They must also be artists, as Darwin was.

Speaking out for biology teachers, Adrian M. Wenner of the University of California (Santa Barbara) is disturbed by creationism:

An issue that would seem trivial has exploded into a problem of national concern. Science is apparently threatened, and biologists seem to be in a bind. Surely all views must be given a platform; to do otherwise is unscientific. Censorship must not be tolerated. But if beliefs are given equal time with facts, where will it all end? How can we teach the truths about science if we are distracted by theology?

. . . Biology is a science: therefore we can insist that *creationism must not be given special treatment.* It must not be sheltered from the scientific scrutiny we eventually bring to all hypotheses and theories. Let teachers hold conferences and gather all the available evidence in support of all available theories and all evidence that contradicts those theories. It will soon become clear that it is not reasonable to spend an equal amount of time on each *theory*. The equal-time concept applies only to the consideration of each item of valid scientific evidence, both positive and negative. The reasons for the demise of some of the early, but now defunct, theories might prove very interesting in a science course.

The year California's State Board of Education made its ruling about presenting creationism as a viable alternative to evolution, Dobzhansky delivered a moving addresss to biology teachers attending the annual National Association of Biology Teachers convention. One of the world's leading geneticists, Dobzhansky holds eighteen honorary doctorates from universities in this country and abroad.

He began his address by telling about sheik Abd el Aziz bin Bas who in 1966 asked the king of Saudi Arabia to suppress a heresy that was spreading in his land. The sheik wrote:

the Holy Koran, the Prophet's teachings, the majority of Islamic scientists, and the actual facts all prove that the Sun is running in its orbit . . . and that the earth is fixed and stable, spread out by God for his mankind. . . . Any one who professed otherwise would utter a charge of falsehood toward God, the Koran, and the Prophet.

Dobzhansky continued:

The good sheik evidently holds the Copernican theory to be a *mere theory*, not a *fact*. A theory can be verified by a mass of facts, but it becomes a proven theory, not a fact. . . . Parts of the Copernican world model, such as the contention that the earth rotates around the sun and not *vice versa*, have not been verified by direct observations. . . . Yet scientists accept the model as an accurate representation of reality. Why? Because it makes sense of a multitude of facts which are otherwise meaningless or extravagant.

Although he may not have been doing so directly, Dobzhansky was answering one of the creationists' chief criticisms of evolutionary biology: their view that evolution cannot be substantiated on the basis of observed facts. "It is obvious," according to Gish, "that no one observed the origin of the universe, the origin of life, the conversion of a fish into an amphibian, or an ape into a man. No one, as a matter of fact, has even observed the origin of a species by naturally occurring processes. Evolution has been *postulated*, but it has never been *observed*."

But Dobzhansky argues: "Why then do we accept the *mere theory* that the earth is a sphere revolving around a spherical sun? Are we simply submitting to authority? Not quite: we know that those who took time to study the evidence found it convincing."

Evidence that points to evolution is invariably turned around by the creationists and used to support their argument, homologues being an example. If the evidence cannot be turned around, then it is tossed aside as "mere unsubstantiated theory," as is the dating of rocks by the radioactive decay method. In that case, observes Dobzhansky:

one can suppose that the Creator saw fit to play deceitful tricks on geologists and biologists. He carefully arranged to have various rocks provided with isotope ratios just right to mislead us into thinking that certain rocks are 2 billion years old, others 2 million, while in fact they are only some 6,000 years old. This kind of pseudo-explanation is not very new. One of the early anti-evolutionists, P. H. Gosse, published a book entitled *Omphalos (The Navel)*. The gist of this amazing book is that

Adam, though he had no mother, was created with a navel, and that fossils were placed by the Creator where we find them now—a deliberate act on His part, to give the appearance of great antiquity and geologic upheavals. It is easy to see the fatal flaw in all such notions. They are blasphemies, accusing God of absurd deceitfulness. This is as revolting as it is uncalled for.

✖✖✖

ACCOUNTING
FOR DIVERSITY

✖✖✖

Commenting on the abundant and wide-ranging diversity of species, Dobzhansky describes a fungus organism (of the family Laboulbeniaceae) so highly specialized that it grows exclusively on the rear portion of a certain species of beetle found only in certain limestone caves in southern France; a fly (*Psilopa petrolei*) whose larval stage develops in crude oil in California, the only known insect able to live and feed in oil; and a species of fly (*Drosophila carcinophila*) whose larval form develops exclusively within certain structures of a land crab found in the Caribbean. "Whence came these extraordinary, seemingly whimsical and superfluous creatures?" asks Dobzhansky.

> The only explanation that makes sense is that the organic diversity has evolved in response to the diversity of environment on the planet earth. . . . All this is understandable in the light of evolution theory; but what a senseless operation it would have been, on God's part, to fabricate a multitude of species *ex nihilo* and then let most of them die out! . . . The organic diversity becomes reasonable and understandable if the Creator has created the living world not by caprice but by evolution

propelled by natural selection. It is wrong to hold creation and evolution as mutually exclusive alternatives. I am a creationist *and* an evolutionist. Evolution is God's, or Nature's, method of Creation. Creation is not an event that happened in 4004 B.C.; it is a process that began some 10 billion years ago and is still under way.

If there were no evolution and each of the millions of species of plants and animals were created individually by God, then we must again accuse God of cheating, Dobzhansky says. The antievolutionists "must insist that He deliberately arranged things exactly as if His method of creation was evolution, intentionally to mislead sincere seekers of truth."

Dobzhansky left his audience with no doubt about where he stands in the evolution debate:

Let me try to make crystal clear what is established beyond reasonable doubt, and what needs further study, about evolution. Evolution as a process that has always gone on in the history of the earth can be doubted only by those who are ignorant of the evidence or are resistant to evidence, owing to emotional blocks or to plain bigotry. By contrast, the mechanisms that bring evolution about certainly need study and clarification. There are no alternatives to evolution as history that can withstand critical examination. Yet we are constantly learning new and important facts about evolutionary mechanisms.

Perhaps the most convincing argument of all, at least for those who are not die-hard fundamentalists, makes it unnecessary to match the creationists point for point. Dobzhansky asks:

Does the evolutionary doctrine clash with religious faith? It does not. It is a blunder to mistake the Holy Scriptures for elementary textbooks of astronomy, geology, biology, and anthropology. Only if symbols are construed to mean what they are

not intended to mean can there arise imaginary, insoluble conflicts. . . . The blunder leads to blasphemy: the Creator is accused of systematic deceitfulness.

Garrett Hardin, speaking at the same NABT convention,
summed up the evolutionists' argument—from the points of
view both of biology as a science and of biology teaching—
when he said:

> the choice between Genesis and Darwinism is not a choice
> between two scientific theories but between one scientific theory
> (Darwinism) and the rejection of rationality. Once you reject
> rationality there is no limit to the number of *explanations* of the
> world, all equally valid *and all equally invalid*. Indeed, there is
> a host of creation myths among the many religions of the world,
> and to single out the story of Genesis for inclusion in the school
> curriculum is to establish a state religion, which the Constitution
> strictly forbids Americans to do.

9

OF LIFE "OUT YONDER IN THE DARK"

*Are we alone in the universe? This question
looms larger than ever today. If we can sample
the alien dust of another world, what hidden
secrets may we not discover? If we scan the radio
waves from a distant galaxy, what may we not
hear if we listen closely? If we probe into the
chemistry of life's origin, what may we not discern
about its possibility elsewhere in the universe?
The search for life beyond the earth is the driving
force of the new science of exobiology.*

—Cyril Ponnamperuma (1972)

With remarkable insight, the Italian monk Giordano
Bruno wrote in the 1500s:

Sky, universe, all-embracing ether, and immeasurable space
alive with movement . . . all these are of one nature. In space
there are countless constellations, suns and planets; we see only
the suns because they give light; the planets remain invisible,

for they are small and dark. There are also numberless earths circling around their suns, no worse and no less inhabited than this globe of ours. For no reasonable mind can assume that heavenly bodies which may be far more magnificent than ours would not bear upon them creatures similar or even superior to those upon our human Earth.

Whether in this century or the next, forms of life other than those known to us on Earth are bound to be discovered elsewhere in the Universe. Low orders of life forms may be discovered on Mars by unmanned space probes, or intelligent beings may make themselves known to us from some Earth-like planet secretly revolving about a star elsewhere in the Galaxy. Inevitably, the day will come when Earthmen discover extraterrestrial life. The big question is not *when,* but "What will it be like?" If the evolutionists are correct, it will be like nothing known to us. If it is, then the whole concept of evolution will be open to serious doubt!

🦋🦋🦋

WHEN IS A THING
A LIVING THING?

🦋🦋🦋

No one can deny that nonliving and living things both are made up of atoms. Oxygen, hydrogen, nitrogen, phosphorous, carbon, potassium, and sodium are among the most important atoms in living systems known to us. But rocks, water, salt, and many other nonliving substances are composed of the same kinds of atoms. What, then, is the difference between those things we call "living" and those we call "nonliving"?

One difference is that nonliving things cannot repair themselves if they are damaged—or can they? Another difference

is that nonliving things cannot reproduce more of their kind—
or can they? Still another difference is that living things are
able to survive drastic changes in their environment by themselves changing over a period of many generations. Let's see.

An electronics engineer would quickly disagree with the first
two differences. He would say that he can design machines
that can repair themselves if damaged and that can assemble
out of an assortment of parts more of their kind. Perhaps so,
in a limited way. But can he design a machine that can adapt
to unpredictable changes in the environment over a period of
millions of years? Unlikely.

When we talk about the difference between living and nonliving things, the important point is not necessarily the kinds
of atoms they contain, but the way those atoms react with each
other and to atoms outside the living system. A living thing is
able to keep itself going by organizing and reorganizing its
billions of atoms from one moment to the next. That is something a piece of quartz, however atomically well ordered it may
be, cannot do.

The smallest unit of life is the cell. Most cells are much
smaller than the dot over this letter *i*. Yet the tiniest cell is able
to carry out all of the essential life functions that you yourself
carry out. The inhospitable terrain of the Moon and of Mars
are better known to us than the inner terrain of the cellular
units that sustain us. Cells have many different parts, each
carrying out certain functions. If one of those parts is damaged
and the damage is not major, the cell repairs itself by selecting
from the external environment the kinds and numbers of atoms
and molecules it needs for repair. That is a remarkable thing.

The cell functions and maintains itself so long as it is able
to keep its atoms and molecules organized. "Organized"—that
is the key word when we speak of life. Outside the cell the

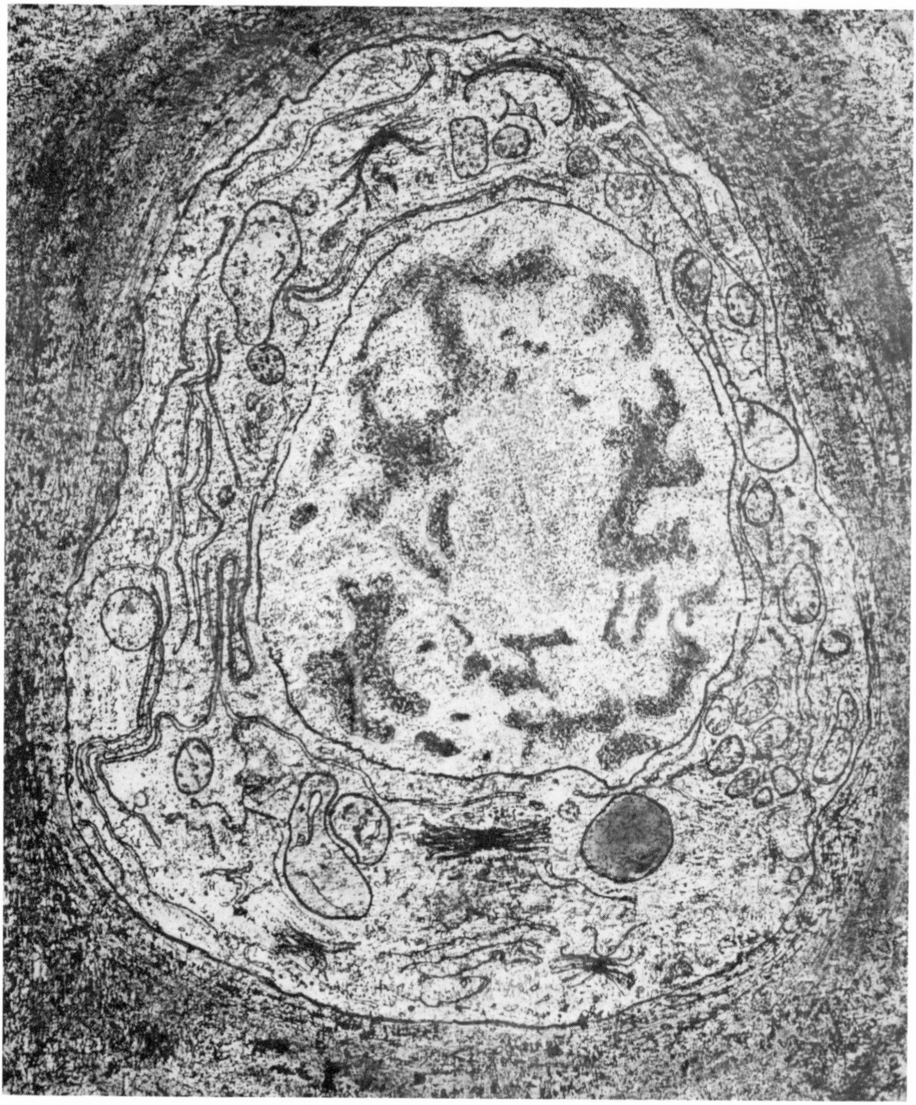

This sketch of a cell, magnified many thousands of times, shows that cells are extremely complex. Each structure, enclosed within its own membrane sac, carries out one or more functions vital to the cell. And the number and distribution of the structures are continually changing to suit the cell's needs. By drawing in materials from the outside, the cell keeps itself in repair, assembling new structures as they are needed. SCIENCE PHOTO/GRAPHICS, LTD.

atoms and molecules cannot organize and reorganize themselves. Either they are in a state of disorder, or, as in crystals,
they are organized but are locked in a fixed pattern unable to
change except by being acted on by some external force. The
cell's protection against the random, disorderly outside world
is a membrane sac. Without that membrane, the orderly arrangement of molecules of the cell would be upset by the inva-
sion of a jumble of atoms and molecules from the outside. The
cell would die, not a slow, but an instant death.

The membrane does not cut the cell off completely from its
outside environment. All over the membrane are openings,
small and large. These windows on the outside world permit
certain molecules to enter the cell, but only when they are
needed, it seems. The windows also permit certain molecules
within the cell, molecules that are not needed, to leave. There
is a continual two-way flow of materials entering and leaving
the cell. As one biologist has put it: "This membrane is the
boundary of life. Inside is an orderly, integrated molecular
society. Outside is the cruel, disorderly world."

Keeping certain kinds and amounts of molecules inside itself, taking in nutrient molecules, ridding itself of waste molecules, repairing itself if damaged, making more cells of its own
pattern, and maintaining its orderly society of molecules amid
the chaotic outside world—these, then, are the processes carried
out by those simplest units of life of which we all are composed.
The cell, tiny though it is, is so marvelously complex that biologists are quite baffled by it. At least, they are baffled if they
try to imagine it springing into being fully formed during one
moment of time when there were no living things. It is possible
to gain complete understanding of the cell only by gaining an
understanding of how the first cells came into being early in
Earth's history some 3 billion or more years ago.

❁❁❁

LIFE
ON OTHER
WORLDS

❁❁❁

Laboratory experiments have suggested certain ways in which the first prebiological cells may have come into being out of chemical raw materials of the environment. They have also shown how those first organized aggregates of molecules might have evolved on a chemical level to more complex and more sophisticated aggregates, for example, those molecular aggregates known as proteins and nucleic acid, two basic molecules for life from bacteria to mammals. The great chain of events that eventually led to the first biological cells with all of the life properties we have been talking about has most of its links missing. Because all of the steps in between present-day life and the first living things on Earth happened so very long ago and because all traces of the earliest living materials presumably have been lost to us, we are hard pressed to guess how the great chain of events gradually led to the complex cells we know today.

One exciting question biologists are asking is whether exploration of the planets will turn up some of the long-lost steps related to the origin of life on Earth. For example, is it possible that life also began on the Moon or on Mars but never developed beyond a certain primitive stage there? If so, possibly we can rewrite certain chapters in the history of life on Earth, a history long since erased by time and its conspirator, the agent of erosion.

The British astronomer Michael W. Ovenden has suggested that possibly we should not look on Mars as an old planet but as "one that is younger than Earth from the point of view of life—and one whose future devolopments may far outstrip evolution on Earth." If he is correct, then Earth scientists of far-off future generations will have the opportunity of witnessing the origin of the simplest living matter and recording its subsequent evolution through some sort of time-lapse documentation, a feat that would span unimaginably long periods of time.

The National Academy of Science has set down the search for life beyond Earth as a major goal of space biology:

It is not since Charles Darwin and, before him, the Polish astronomer Nicolaus Copernicus, that science has had the opportunity for so great an impact on man's understanding of man. The scientific question at stake in space biology is the most exciting, the most challenging and profound issue, not only in this century, but of the entire naturalistic movement that has characterized the history of western thought for over three thousand years. If there is life on Mars and if we can demonstrate its independent origin, then we shall have an enlightening answer to the question of the improbability and uniqueness in the origin of life. Arising twice in a single planetary system, it must surely occur abundantly elsewhere in the staggering number of comparable planetary systems.

Biologists do not know if Earth-type biology is necessarily the only type. For example, what if biologists discovered chemical building blocks on Mars fundamentally different from those on Earth? This would suggest the possibility that life arose independently on Mars, that it was not carried across space from one planet to another, a method considered unlikely by some exobiologists. If in only one planetary system life arose independently on two different planets, think of what this means when we consider our entire galaxy of upward of 100 billion stars! Astronomers estimate that there are roughly 600

❋ *The Andromeda Galaxy (NGC 224) is a spiral galaxy like our own but about twice as large and lying at a distance of some two million light-years (or 12,000,000,000,000,000,000 miles). The two bright patches are smaller, satellite galaxies.* MOUNT WILSON AND PALOMAR OBSERVATORIES

✵ The number of galaxies in the heavens is staggering to the imagination. A good telescope brings into view more galaxies than the number of stars that can be seen with the naked eye. The cluster of galaxies shown here is visible in the constellation Hercules.

MOUNT WILSON AND PALOMAR OBSERVATORIES

million planets in our own galaxy capable of supporting life, including some form of intelligent life. If that is so, there must be trillions of planetary systems throughout the Universe. The present estimate is that 5 percent of all stars in the Universe have at least one planet with an environment suitable for life. That means there are 10^{18} (1,000,000,000,000,000,000) possibilities! Now we begin to walk that narrow line separating science from science fiction. But walk it we must, since that is the way our reasoning leads us.

According to Robert L. Sinsheimer, a biologist at the California Institute of Technology, there is no reason for us to suppose that there is only one possible grouping of molecules that can organize themselves into a living system. When life arose on Earth, there happened to be certain kinds of molecules around and water as a liquid medium. Even though we do not know of any, we can admit the possibility of other kinds of molecules organizing themselves into living systems associated with a different liquid medium. Sinsheimer has written:

> Life might occur in other forms and in other chemistry, perhaps on another scale of size or in another tempo of time. Here I have the uneasy feeling that with perhaps less insight but also with perhaps more imagination the writers of science-fiction have been here long before us [biologists]. . . . And so we look out to the stars for another sign of awareness. Do the stars look back? Is there perhaps on some far distant planet a writer now describing his kind of life and proving that a life form such as ours could hardly be? Perhaps.

If evolution is the great driving force of life, there must be a near limitless variety of ways in which living molecular aggregates could arrange themselves and over millions of years change into a variety of life forms very different from our own. In short, it would be unthinkable that evolution on any two planets in our galaxy, or elsewhere in the Universe, has followed the same pattern exactly. "The precise accidental duplication of a complex form of life is extremely unlikely to occur in even the same environment," according to the biologist Loren Eiseley, "let alone in the different background and atmosphere of a far-off world. The statistical probability of its precise reduplication on another planet is so small as to be meaningless."

As the biochemist Isaac Asimov and his coauthor Stephen Dole have put it in their book *Planets for Man*:

When it comes to the living things [of] other planets, of course, these might differ widely, depending on the precise course that evolution happened to take in each special circumstance. Even so, on each planet one would expect to find organisms carrying on photosynthesis and creatures capable of invading practically every conceivable corner of the environment: marine forms, fresh-water creatures, land creatures, aerial forms, cave organisms, and so on. In spite of differences in detail, certain basic kinds of life forms would be expected to display some common characteristics. Thus, fast-swimming marine forms would be streamlined [such as our sharks and porpoises]. Land animals would typically have legs, and fast-moving aerial forms would have wings. . . . On no other planet, however, would we expect to find any of the [same biological groupings] of plants or animals with which we are familiar on the surface of Earth. From the smallest virus to the largest whale, the Earthly life forms are unique products of Earth. Each planet on which living things have evolved must have its own peculiar classification of organisms, and this in itself should present the human race in general and biologists in particular with endless realms of new wonder and experience.

Eiseley, in his book *The Immense Journey,* echoes the same thought eloquently in these words:

Life, even cellular life, may exist out yonder in the dark. But high or low in nature, it will not wear the shape of man. That shape is the evolutionary product of a strange, long wandering through the attics of the forest roof, and so great are the chances of failure, that nothing precisely and identically human is likely ever to come that way again.

Lights come and go in the night sky. Men, troubled at last by the things they build, may toss in their sleep and dream bad dreams, or lie awake while the meteors whisper greenly overhead. But nowhere in all space or on a thousand worlds will there be men to share our loneliness. There may be wisdom; there may be power; somewhere across space great instruments, handled by strange manipulative organs may stare vainly at our floating cloud wrack, their owners yearning as we yearn. Nevertheless, in the nature of life and in the principles of evolution we have had our answer. Of men elsewhere, and beyond, there will be none forever.

BOOKS FOR
FURTHER READING

In selecting books for further reading, I have tried to keep the general reader in mind and accordingly have listed what I consider to be a variety of titles at once informative and interesting. Some readers may wonder why I have not included A. I. Oparin's classic book, *The Origin of Life on the Earth,* or Simpson's *The Meaning of Evolution,* or Shklovskii's and Sagan's *Intelligent Life in the Universe,* or any of a dozen other advanced titles that come to mind. I have not simply because this book is not intended as a text but as an introduction to some of the major concepts in the continuing creationism-evolution debate, concepts that must be grasped if a meaningful discussion of the controversy is to take place.

ALLEN, TOM. *The Quest.* Philadelphia: Chilton Books, 1965. A fine introduction to the search for extraterrestrial life, written on the popular level and ranging through astronomical mythology, alien life, and manned and unmanned exploration of worlds beyond our own.
ASIMOV, ISAAC, AND DOLE, STEPHEN. *Planets for Man.* New York: Random House, Inc., 1964. A nontechnical survey based on The Rand Corporation Research Study, "Habitable Planets for Man." Human requirements for life are discussed in relation to the properties of other planets, and hence their habitability by man. The

nearest planetary candidates are discussed as is the would-be future of people on a planet environmentally different from our own.

AULIE, RICHARD P. "The Doctrine of Special Creation," *The American Biology Teacher* (April and May 1972). A hard look, by a historian of biology and medicine, at the science and philosophy of the Creation Research Society, as reflected in its textbook *Biology: A Search for Order in Complexity*.

BERGSON, HENRI. *The Two Sources of Morality and Religion*. New York: Henry Holt and Company, Inc., 1935. One of the famous French philosopher's greatest works. The function of man's myth-making ability is examined in many contexts. Decidedly advanced reading.

CALVIN, MELVIN. *Chemical Evolution*. New York: Oxford University Press, 1969. The subtitle of this technical volume adequately describes its contents: "Molecular Evolution Towards the Origin of Living Systems on the Earth and Elsewhere."

DARWIN, CHARLES. *The Voyage of the Beagle*. Garden City, N.Y.: Doubleday & Company, Inc., 1962. This edition of Darwin's own account of his observations and thinking during the *Beagle's* five-year voyage around the world contains annotations by the science writer Leonard Engle. Nontechnical, Darwin's account of the voyage is as absorbing as a good novel.

DOBZHANSKY, THEODOSIUS. "Nothing in Biology Makes Sense Except in the Light of Evolution," *The American Biology Teacher* (March 1973). This world-renowned geneticist speaks out for evolution in the creationism *versus* evolution debate.

EISELEY, LOREN. *The Immense Journey*. New York: Random

House, Inc., 1959. An eloquently written story of man told by a scientist who is at once an anthropologist and a visionary. Nontechnical.

FENTON, CARROLL LANE and MILDRED ADAMS. *Giants of Geology.* Garden City, N.Y.: Doubleday & Company, Inc., 1952. As its title suggests, this popular and highly readable survey reviews the work of a number of outstanding geologists, from classical Greece to twentieth-century America.

GALLANT, ROY A. *Charles Darwin, the Making of a Scientist.* Garden City, N.Y.: Doubleday & Company, Inc., 1972. A concise biography of Darwin, with emphasis on his observations during the *Beagle's* voyage.

———. *Man's Reach for the Stars.* Garden City, N.Y.: Doubleday & Company, Inc., 1971. A nontechnical account of the preparation of men and machines for the exploration of space beyond the Solar System.

GISH, DUANE T. *Evolution, the Fossils Say No!* San Diego, California: ICR (Institute for Creation Research) Publishing Company, 1973. One of the leading spokesmen for the Creation Research Society presents in nontechnical language that group's position on evolution.

———. "Creation, Evolution, and the Historical Evidence," *The American Biology Teacher* (March 1973). The creationists are given equal time in this educational journal to present their views in a series of articles about the evolution *versus* creation controversy. The Institute for Creation Research, P.O. Box 15486, San Diego, California 92115, offers a variety of literature and cassettes for sale.

GOODRICH, NORMA LORRE. *The Ancient Myths.* New York: The New American Library, 1960. A retelling of myths from Sumer, Egypt, Crete and Greece, Troy, Persia and Afghanistan, India, and Rome.

GRABINER, JUDITH V., and MILLER, PETER D. "Effects of the Scopes Trial," *Science*, 6 September 1974. These researchers (the first a historian of science and the second a mathematics teacher) report on their analysis of the treatment of evolution and Darwin in high school science textbooks from the decade of the Scopes trial to the late 1960s.

GRAVES, ROBERT. *The Greek Myths*, 2 vols. London: Penguin Books, 1964. A scholarly review and commentary on the Greek myths.

HARDIN, GARRETT. "Ambivalent Aspects of Evolution," *The American Biology Teacher* (January 1973). A biologist speaks out on evolution in the ongoing debate between creationism and evolution.

HOTTON, NICHOLAS. *The Evidence of Evolution*. New York: American Heritage Publishing Company, 1968. A semipopular presentation of the significant evidence for the evolution of species through natural selection.

IRVINE, WILLIAM. *Apes, Angels, and Victorians*. New York: McGraw-Hill Book Company, 1955. The social, religious, geological, and biological climates of Darwin's period are described engagingly in this comprehensive account of the early conflict spawned by Darwinism.

LEACH, MARIA. *The Beginning, Creation Myths Around the World*. New York: Funk & Wagnalls Company, 1956. The title adequately describes the contents of this delightful little book.

MALINOWSKY, BRONISLAW. *Magic, Science and Religion*. Garden City, N.Y.: Doubleday & Company, Inc., 1954. An anthropologist looks at humans as reasoning animals, the art of magic and the role of faith and, of special importance in the context of the present book, myth in primitive psychology.

MIDDLETON, JOHN, ed. *Myth and Cosmos.* Garden City, N.Y.: The Natural History Press, 1967. An anthropologist selects professional writings from several of his colleagues and presents various perspectives on myths and symbols. Among the eighteen papers is one entitled "Genesis as Myth."

MILLER, STANLEY L., and ORGEL, LESLIE E. *The Origins of Life on the Earth.* Englewood Cliffs, N.J.: Prentice-Hall, Inc., 1974. A college-level account of the interdisciplinary nature of the search for the origins of life. Miller is one of the pioneer experimenters in the synthesis of simple organic compounds in a primitive Earth environment.

MUNITZ, MILTON K. *Theories of the Universe.* Glencoe, Ill.: The Free Press & The Falcon's Wing Press, 1957. A scholarly work in which theories of the Universe are recounted, from Babylonian myth to modern science.

OVENDEN, MICHAEL W. *Life in the Universe.* Garden City, N.Y.: Doubleday & Company, Inc., 1962. In a semi-popular vein a British astronomer considers the possibility of life elsewhere in the Universe, after analyzing Earth's environment in the context of life's origin and evolution here.

PIAGET, JEAN. *Play, Dreams and Imitation in Childhood.* New York: W.W. Norton & Company, Inc., 1962. The noted French linguist, who has worked extensively with young children, suggests that we may find a number of clues about the workings of the primitive mind by studying symbolism in the play and dreams of children. This is a scholarly and technical work.

PONNAMPERUMA, CYRIL. *The Origins of Life.* New York: E.P. Dutton, 1972. An excellent semipopular account of life's possible origin from chemical raw materials. Also considers the possibility of life elsewhere in the Universe. One of the book's features is its emphasis on methods of investigating the various phenomena it describes.

————. *Exobiology.* New York: American Elsevier Publishing Company, Inc., 1972. A highly technical volume intended for the researcher and advanced student. Part I considers the origin of life on Earth, and Part II considers life beyond Earth.

WENNER, ADRIAN M. "Adam and Eve in Science," *The American Biology Teacher* (May 1973). A biology teacher takes an introspective view of how biology is being taught during the ongoing debate between creationism and evolution.

YOUNG, RICHARD S. *Extraterrestrial Biology.* New York: Holt, Rinehart and Winston, Inc., 1966. In this popular presentation of space biology, the author seeks answers to two questions: "What can our knowledge of biology contribute to the exploration of space?" And, "What can the study of the extraterrestrial environment contribute to our understanding of life and its processes?"

INDEX

Abel, 44
aborigines, Australian, 4
Abraham (Biblical), 47
Adam, 43–44
"Age of Fishes," 109
Ahura Mazda, 36
American Association for the Advancement of Science, 171–72
American Scientific Affiliation, 153
amino acids, 113
amphibians, 109
An (Sumerian god), 34
Anaximander, 52–53
animalcules, 99
Anshar, 20
Apsu, 18
Aramazd, 36
Ararat, Mount, 46–47
Ararat Project, 159
Areg, 36
Aristotle, 56
Artist, Russell C., 167
Asimov, Isaac, 199

Ask, 32
atomic theory,
  in Democritus, 56–58
  in Lucretius, 56, 58–64
"atomic clocks,"
  difficulties with, 74–75
  importance of, 72
  operation of, 73
Atum, 33
Aulie, Richard P., 173
Aziz bin Bas, shiek Abd el, 184

Babel, Tower of, 32
Babylonians, 17–18
  creation myth of, 17–24
  gods of, 19
Bagobo (folktale), 30
Bahía Blanca, 135
"basic kinds." *See* species
Beagle, H.M.S., 133
Beer, Sir Gavin de, 134
Bergson, Henri, 8–9
Bernal, J. D., 110–12
big-bang theory, 90–93

Biology: A Search for Order in
    Complexity (CRS), 160, 177
Bondi, Herman, 90
Boyle, Robert, 56
Brahe, Tycho, 68
Brongniart, Alexandre, 103–
    104
Bruno, Giordano, 189–90
Buffon, George L. de, 126–27

Cain, 44
California Academy of Science,
    181–82
California State Board of Edu-
    cation, 165–70
Cape Verde Islands, 134
Castaneda, Carlos, 6
catastrophism, 104, 130–33,
    158, 182
    critique of, 175–77
cell, the, 191, 193
    development of, 194–95. See
    also prebiological cell
Chatham Islands, 139–42
chordates, the, 157
"coacervates," 115–17
Columbus (Ohio) Board of Ed-
    ucation, 165–66
Copernicus, Nicolaus, 195
    and the Solar System, 66, 68
    and the Sun, 66, 68
creationists,
    Aulie on, 173–74
    critique of evolution by, 154–
    57

on design in nature, 173–75
on environmental adaption,
    144
and evolutionists, 163–70,
    182–84
and the Noachian flood, 158–
    159
on radioactive dating, 157
and species variation, 162–63
supporters of, 152–53
views on species, 159–62
creation myths,
    of Babylonians, 17–24
    and the Bible, 22–23, 32, 142
    of Chinese, 29–30
    classes of, 29
    of the Congo, 32
    decline of, 51–52
    development of language and,
        43–44
    of Egyptians, 33–34
    and the Enuma Elish, 18,
        20–29
    Judeo-Christian tradition and,
        37–50
    in Lucretius, 59–60, 63–64
    from Philippines, 30
    place of man in, 40
    of Pomo Indians, 30–32
    role of the Sun in, 34
    of Scandinavia, 32
    of Sumerians, 24–29
    of Yuchi Indians, 35–36
Creation Research Society
    (CRS), 148, 153–54, 157–

159, 163, 167, 173–76, 180–183. *See also* creationists
cretaceous seas, 109
CRS. *See* Creation Research Society
Cuvier, Baron, 158
Cuvier, George, 103–105, 130, 155

Darwin, Charles, 41, 94, 126–128, 195
and Alfred Wallace, 150
creationist criticism of, 144–145
excavations by, 135, 137
experimental approach of, 143–49
on natural selection, 150
species compared by, 139–41
voyage of, 133–42
Works: *The Natural Selection, The Origin of the Species. See also* evolution and species
Darwin, Erasmus, 127
Darwinism. *See* evolution
Democritus, 56–58
dinosaurs, 109
divine creation. *See* creationists
DNA, 174
Dobzhansky, Theodosius, 150, 161, 171, 184–87
Dole, Stephen, 199

Ea, 20–21, 27
Easter, 12, 15

Eden, Dr. Murray, 169
Edwards, Judge George, 167
Egyptians,
gods of, 33
creation myths of, 33–34
Eiseley, Loren, 199–200
elements (chemical), 83–84
Embla, 32
Empedocles, 54, 56
Enki. *See* Ea
Enlil, 18, 22, 24–25
Enoch, 44
Enos, 44
Enuma Elish, 18, 20–29, 52
animism in, 23–24
conflict in, 21
elements of, 18–19
the flood in, 46
Jacobsen interpretation of, 23–24
and Judeo-Christian tradition compared, 37
opening lines of, 20
second creation in, 23–24
Eostre, 12
Epicurus, 58
Epperson, Susan, 165
Eve, 44
evolution, theory of, 171–73
Aulie on, 173–74
court trials involving, 163–70
creationists and, 154–57, 163–70
Dobzhansky on, 184–86
and Erasmus Darwin, 127

and George de Buffon, 126–127
initial reaction to, 122–23, 148
Jean de Lamarck and, 127, 129
the Koran and, 184
role of environment in, 141–142
species development in, 180–182
and species variety, 162–63, 186–87. See also Charles Darwin, *Origin of the Species*, Scopes trial, and species

Evolution, the Fossils Say No! (CRS), 153–54

First Great Civilizations, The (Hawkes), 16
FitzRoy, Captain, 133
Flood, the, 32, 158–59, 175–76
in the *Enuma Elish*, 46
Flora (Roman goddess), 12
Ford, Dr. John R., 152
fossils,
confusion surrounding, 129–130
creationist view of, 155–57
early study of, 102
interpretations of, 108–109, 138
oldest known, 119
superstitions concerning, 102

Galápagos Islands, 139
galaxies,
origin of, 76
movements of, 92
Galileo, 77
Gamow, George, 92
Geb, 33–34
geological time scale, 104–105
Gilgamesh legend, 45, 177
flood in, 47
Gish, Duane T., 152–53, 156
Gold, Thomas, 90
Goldschmidt, Richard B., 168
Gosse, P. H., 185–86
Grabiner, Judith V., 151
Great Time, 4, 6
Greenland, 75–76
Groton, John M., 44

Hamilton, Sen. Milton, 167
Hanno, 52
Hardin, Garrett, 149, 183, 188
Hawkes, Jacquetta, 16
Helmont, J. B. van, 95
Heraclitus, 54
Hercules, Pillars of, 52
Hertzka, Katherine, 179
"homologues," 181
Hood, Robin, 12
Hoyle, Fred, 90
Hutton, James, 123, 158

Immense Journey, The (Eiseley), 199–200

Institute for Creation Research, 153
Intelligence
  and myth-making compared, 8–9
  and superstition, 9–10
Isis, 33–34

Jablot, Louis, 99–100
Jacobsen, Thorkild, 23–24
James Islands, 139–42
Jastrow, Robert, 90
Java man, 4
Jehovah, 32, 37
Judeo-Christian tradition, creation in,
  compared with *Enuma Elish*, 37
  events of, 38–42
Jung, Carl G., 9

Kant, Immanuel, 77–78, 80
Karoo formation, 159
Keeling Islands, 142
Khnum, 34
Ki, 24–25, 34
Kingu, 27
Kishar, 20
Koran, the, 184
Kuiper, Gerard, 78, 80

Lahamu, 19–20
Lahmu, 19–20
Lamech, 44

Lamarck, Jean Baptiste de, 127–129
Leeuwenhoek, Anton van, 99
Lemaître, Father, 92
Leucippus, 56
Liverpool, 108
life,
  amino acids and, 113
  beginnings of, 110–20
  chemical evolution of, 115–116
  nonliving materials and, 190–191, 193
  in other worlds, 194–200
  and prebiological cells, 117
  role of the Sun in the beginning of, 112–13
  spontaneous generation of, 96–101: *See also* creationists, creation myths, evolution, and species
Lucretius, 58–64, 95–96
  concept of Universe in, 62–63
  creation myth in, 59–60, 63–64
  on nature of matter, 60–63
Lyell, Charles, 123, 131, 148, 158, 180, 182

Madumda, 30, 44
Manchester, 145–46
Marduk, 18, 22–23, 27, 38
Masked God Society, 6
May Day, 12

Mayas, the, 43
Mayr, Ernst, 161
Megatherium, 135–37
Memmius, 58
meteorites, 72
Miller, Peter, 151
Miller, Stanley, 112–13
Morris, Henry, 153, 159
Moses, 47
M60 (galaxy), 91
myth making
  and Carl Jung, 9
  functions of, 6, 8
  and Great Time, 6, 8, 12
  and intelligence compared, 8–10
  and origin of Easter, 14–15
  Pueblo Indians and, 10
  role of anthropomorphism in, 11–12
  and science compared, 15–16
  and the Sun, 14–15
  and the Zuni Indians, 6
mythology. *See* myth making

Nammu, 34
National Academy of Science, 173
natural selection, 146–47
  appeal of, 149–50, Darwin on, 150. *See also* Charles Darwin, and evolution
Natural Selection, The (Darwin), 148
Natural Theology (Paley), 131

Neanderthal man, 4
nebular hypothesis, 77–83
Nepthys, 33–34
Newell, Norman D., 172
Newton, Isaac, 77–78
Nippur, city of, 27
Nizir (mountain), 45
Noah, 22, 32, 44–47
Noachian flood. *See* the Flood
Nudimmut. *See* Ea
Nun (primeval ocean), 33
Nut, 33–34

Odin, 32
Omphalos (Gosse), 185–86
On the Nature of Things (Lucretius), 58
Oparin, A. I., 51, 95, 115–16, 119–20
Ordovician period, 157
Origin of Species by Means of Natural Selection, or the Preservation of the Favoured Races in the Struggle for Life, The (Darwin), 124, 126, 148–50
Ostara, 12
Owen, Richard, 180–81

passing-time, 4, 6
Pasteur, Louis, 100–101
Paley, Williams, 131
P'an Ku, 29–30
Patagonian coast, 138
Pekin Man, 4

Piaget, Jean, 6, 8
Planets for Man (Asimov, Dole), 199
Pleistocene age, 4, 105
pneuma, 54
Pomo Indians, 30–32, 44–45
Ponnamperuma, Cyril, 118, 120, 189
prebiological cells,
    formation of, 116–17
    and living cells, 117
    nutrients of, 117
    role of, in beginning of life, 117. *See also* the cell
Precambrian Period, 109–110
Priestley, J. B., 2
Principles of Geology (Lyell), 180, 182
Ptah, 34

Ra-Amon, 34
radioactive dating, 157
radioactive elements, 73–76
Redt, Francesco, 97–98
Robinson, R. A., 179

Santa María Island, 139
stars,
    birth of, 92
    death of, 88
    function of, 84, 87
    life cycle of, 87–89
Sarton, George, 57
Scopes, John, 151, 163, 165
Scopes trial, 151, 163, 165

Seth, 44
Shu, 33–34
Silurian Period, 105
Simpson, George Gaylord, 123–124, 161
Sinsheimer, Robert L., 198
Smith, Williams, 102–103
Socrates, 41
Solar System,
    and the "atomic clock," 72
    and the catastrophism, 77
    Copernicus on, 66, 68
    dating of, 71–76
    early theories of, 66–69
    Kant on, 77–78, 80
    Kuiper on, 78, 80
    and the nebular hypothesis, 77–83
    Newton on, 77–78
    origins of, 76–83
    Weizsäcker on, 78, 80
solar wind, 83
species, 173–74
    adaption within, 145–47
    view of creationists on, 159–162
    definition of, 161
    the Noachian flood and, 158
    numbers of, 120–21
    relative size of, 121
    variations within, 162–63, 186–88. *See also* evolution
spontaneous generation of life, 96–101
steady-state theory, 89–90

Sumerians,
  creation myth of, 24–29
  gods of, 25
Sun, the, 14
  Copernicus on, 66, 68
  formation of, 80–81, 83
  study of, 71–72
supernova, 87
supernebulae, 88
superstition, 8–9
Swinton, William Elgin, 109

Tefnut, 33–34
Texas State Textbook Commission, 165
Thales, 52
Ti'amat, 18, 27, 38
Tibetan Plateau, 158–59
Toxodon, 135–37
Tsohaya. *See* Yuchi Indians
Tyndall, John, 119

uniformitarianism, 158, 182–83
Universe, concepts of,
  in Anaximander, 52–53

in Anaximenes, 54
big-bang theory and, 90–93
in Lucretius, 62–63
steady-state theory and, 89–90
in Thales, 52
Ur of the Chaldees, 176
Ussher, Archbishop James, 42

Vergil, 95
Vinci, Leonardo da, 102

Wallace, Alfred Russell, 147–148
Weizsäcker, Carl von, 78, 80
Wenner, Adrian M., 183
Woolley, Sir Leonard, 176

Xenophanes, 102

Ymir, 32
Young, Keith, 179
Yuchi Indians, 35–36

Zuni Indians, 6